Book 3

Right into Reading

A Phonics-Based Reading and Comprehension Program

Jane Ervin

Illustrations by Tatjana Mai-Wyss

Educators Publishing Service
Cambridge and Toronto

About the Author

Jane Ervin works in Washington, D.C., with children with reading and learning differences, and advises parents on educational concerns. Dr. Ervin has written more than 30 books for students, teachers, and parents; her workbooks have sold over 5 million copies. She received her Ed.D. and postdoctoral diploma from UCLA.

Acknowledgements

I would like to thank Paul Ervin for his contribution to several stories and cartoons in *Right into Reading, Book 3*. I also wish to thank Jo Ann Dyer for the typing and preparation of the manuscript.

Acquiring Editor: Sethany Rancier Alongi
Design: Karen Lomigora
Typesetting: Sarah Rakitin
Editor: Wendy Drexler
Managing Editor: Sheila Neylon

Educators Publishing Service
800.225.5750
www.epsbooks.com

Printed in U.S.A.

ISBN 978-0-8388-2605-8

4 5 6 MLY 10 09

CONTENTS

PART THREE: A Variety of Sounds

LESSON

Part One: New Sounds or No Sounds

Lesson 1: Soft G
page 1

Lesson 2: Soft C
page 12

Lesson 3: Ph
page 26

Lesson 4: Silent Letters
page 41

Lesson 5: Syllables
page 56

Lesson 1: Soft G

When **g** is followed by **e, i,** or **y,** it has the **j** sound.

 giraffe

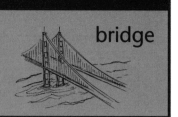 bridge

Sound out the letters to read each word.

age	huge	gem	page
gym	germs	wage	large
change	stage	charge	rage

Egypt	urge	magic	margin
hinge	giant	ginger	agent
legend	passage	message	energy

In these words, the **d** sound is not pronounced.

edge	badge	judge	pledge
fudge	bridge	ledge	trudge

These words do not follow the rule. They have the regular **g** sound.

give	girl	get	guess
gift	finger	tiger	anger

→ Draw a line between the words that have the **j** sound for **g.**

giant	goat	age	gym	good	give	sing	margin
gum	giraffe	gate	dog	magic	agent	germ	got

→ Circle the name of the picture.

gem germ	wage page	margin magic
budge badge	giant ginger	fudge judge
girl gift	gym agent	passage message

→ Add **g** to find the name of each picture. Write the number of the picture in the box. Then circle the sound that **g** has: **g** or **j**.

☐	g j	sta___e
☐	g j	___irl
☐	g j	ti___er
☐	g j	fin___er

☐	g j	hin___e
☐	g j	mar___in
☐	g j	___iraffe
☐	g j	brid___e

1.

2.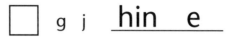

3.

4.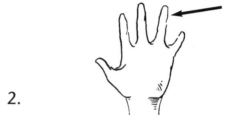

5.

6.

7.

8.

→ Read the words in the box. Then read the riddles. On the line, write the word that answers each riddle.

gem	gym	fudge	bridge
margin	huge	germs	giraffe

1. They can make you sick. _____

2. You cross it to get to the other side. _____

3. It is a candy. _____

4. It is a jewel. _____

5. You can work out here. _____

6. This is an animal with a long neck. _____

7. It means very large. _____

8. It is on the side of the page. _____

Upset George

→ Read each sentence and circle the missing word. Then write the word on the line.

George, _____ nine, is generally in a good mood.

    agent   aged

But today he is angry and all on _____.

    ledge   edge

He made some _____ mistakes in his math homework.

    huge   urge

He read the wrong _____ for English.

    stage   page

He forgot to change his shoes for _____ .

    gym   gem

Finally, the _____ broke on his locker door.

    hedge   hinge

All his books fell into the _____.

    message   passage

At this stage, he had the _____ to throw all the books away.

    urge   margin

Instead, he put them into his backpack and _____ home.

    judged   trudged

At home his mom had left him a _____ .

    message   magic

"I have managed to _____ tickets for the game!"

    give   get

Things began to look better.

Some Facts about Egypt

What is Egypt? Circle the answer that you think is correct.

(a) It is the name of a person.

(b) It is a land in Africa.

(c) It is a dinosaur.

 Read the passage to find out.

Egypt is a country in the northeastern corner of Africa.

A large, long river (900 miles long!) called the Nile runs the length of Egypt. It is like a giant snake that acts as a passageway between the south and the north. The land at the edge of the Nile is the most inhabited. This is because the waters of the Nile make the desert land rich and fertile so that people can grow crops here.

Today, a huge dam controls the waters of the Nile. In ages past, summer rains caused the Nile to over-flow, bringing water to the region. The floods were usually good for the Egyptians. But if the floods were too low for several years, crops would not grow. If the floods were too high, they would destroy the villages.

Egypt

In those ages past, the Egyptians (i-jip'-shens) depended on the Nile for every part of their lives. Even their reli-gion (ri-lij'-en) followed the changes in the river. The people said that the river was a gift given to them by the gods.

Did you guess what Egypt is? Circle the correct answer.

      (a) It is the name of a person.

      (b) It is a land in Africa.

      (c) It is a dinosaur.

→ Checking up on your reading. Circle the correct answer.

1. Egypt is in the

      (a) southwestern corner of Africa.

      (b) northeastern corner of Africa.

2. The river Nile flows between

      (a) the south and the north.

      (b) the east and the west.

3. Most Egyptians live

      (a) in villages.

      (b) near the Nile River.

4. The Nile River is important to the Egyptians because

      (a) its waters make the land rich and fertile so people can grow crops.

      (b) it has many fish that the Egyptians like to eat.

5. In the past, the summer rains were not always good for the people because

      (a) they made the gods angry.

      (b) they could flood and destroy villages.

6. The Egyptians said that the Nile River

      (a) divided their land into two parts.

      (b) was a gift given to them by the gods.

Egypt's Pyramids

How did the Egyptians build these giant structures?

 Read the story to find out.

The pyramids were built **thousands** of years ago in Egypt. How did they manage to build these giant **structures** made from huge blocks of stone?

It was a difficult task. In those days the Egyptians had only the simplest tools. They did not have wheels or animals to help them lift or carry heavy loads. They **succeeded** in building the pyramids because they were clever **engineers** and because they had plenty of workers—thousands of men were sent from the villages to work on the pyramids.

This is how modern experts guess that the Great Pyramid of Khufu was built in about 2600 B.C.—which is still the largest stone **structure** ever constructed. First, the huge stone blocks were carried on wooden sleds to the Nile River. Then the blocks were loaded onto flat **barges** and floated down to where the pyramid was to be built. Each stone was painted with a message telling where it was to be placed in the pyramid.

The base of the pyramid was cut into a rocky hill that stuck out from the **desert**. It was a perfect square. Huge, flat steps were cut out of the **uneven** rock to make it level. Then the stones were carefully arranged one on top of the other according to their markings.

→ Checking up: See if you are getting the facts. Circle the correct answer.

1. The pyramids were built a hundred years ago.   (a) yes   (b) no

2. The wheel had not been invented when the   (a) yes   (b) no
   pyramids were built.

3. The Egyptians were clever engineers but they still   (a) yes   (b) no
   needed many men to build the pyramids.

4. Barges took the huge stones down the Nile River.   (a) yes   (b) no

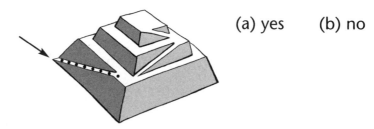

5. Each stone was marked to show where it was to go in the pyramid.   (a) yes   (b) no

 How did the men get the huge stones where they had to go on the pyramid? It is thought that they used ramps that were built in **tiers** (see the drawing) that went up the four sides of the pyramid. Three ramps went up, and one went down. Blocks of stone were dragged up and set into place. Then the workers cut down the blocks to form smooth, sloping sides. Each ramp began at one corner (see arrow) and ended at the top. The dotted line shows the path of one ramp.

The work of hauling the stones required strong men with much energy. It was hard, hot work in the desert sun, and they were not paid any wages. The men worked in gangs of 18 to 20. People now think that the men were not slaves but were willing workers because the pyramid was for their king.

→ Circle the correct answer.

1. How many ramps were there?

   (a) 3

   (b) 4

2. The ramps went

   (a) straight up.

   (b) in tiers or levels.

3. The work of hauling the stones up the ramps was done by

   (a) men.

   (b) oxen.

4. The man were paid

   (a) a lot of money.

   (b) no wages.

5. The men were most likely

(a) slaves made to do the work.

(b) Egyptians who were willing to do the work.

6. The pyramid was built

(a) in the desert.

(b) on fertile land.

➔ Match the words with their meanings.

_____	1. something built	(a) tiers
_____	2. a series of rows	(b) desert
_____	3. a dry, sandy region	(c) succeed
_____	4. to be able to do what was planned	(d) a structure

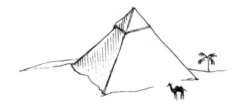

_____	5. a flat-bottomed boat	(e) an engineer
_____	6. ten times one hundred	(f) uneven
_____	7. not level	(g) one thousand
_____	8. a person who plans or builds machinery, roads, bridges, and buildings	(h) a barge

The kings of Egypt designed buildings called pyramids. If you could design a building, what would it look like? Write your description here.

_____

_____

_____

_____

_____

_____

_____

_____

_____

_____

_____

_____

_____

_____

_____

Lesson 2: Soft C

When **c** is followed by
e, i, or **y,** it has the **s** sound.

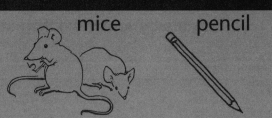

mice   pencil

Sound out the letters to read each word.

ice	race	cent	face
fence	nice	place	since
space	icy	slice	dance
city	price	sauce	rice

trace	recess	center	decide
glance	concert	cancel	circus
peace	cereal	voice	graceful
recent	certain	juice	Pacific

➜ Match the words with their meanings.

_____ 1. one hundred years   (a) decide

_____ 2. to make up your mind   (b) to conceal

_____ 3. to hide   (c) century

_____ 1. very, very good   (a) Pacific

_____ 2. sure   (b) certain

_____ 3. an ocean   (c) excellent

_____ 1. What we are made up of   (a) cells

_____ 2. We do this on birthdays   (b) to cease

_____ 3. to stop   (c) celebrate

➜ Circle the name of the picture.

race face space	circus certain city	prance dance France	braces traces laces
price rice ice	cell cent center	concert cancel pencil	cereal celery century

➜ Read each sentence and circle the correct word.

1. Every July 4 Americans (celebrate, decide) Independence Day.

2. America has had its independence for over two (centers, centuries).

3. American (cents, citizens) were at war with one another during the Civil War.

4. Lewis and Clark crossed the United States from 1804 to1806 and reached the (Pacific, France) Ocean.

5. The (icy, city) of Washington, D.C. was a wet swamp before it became the capital of the United States.

6. Recently, (traces, spaces) of dinosaurs have been found in the capital of the United States.

→ Draw a line to the correct ending of each sentence. Then put an X in the box next to the sentence that tells about the picture.

	Celia put ice	over her rice.
	Cynthia poured sauce	on her cereal.
	Cindy poured milk	into her juice.

	Astronauts train	to sing in concerts.
	Acrobats practice	to go into space.
	Singers train their voices	to perform in the circus.

☐ The amount of time for recess is   1 mile.

☐ The length of the race is   75 cents.

☐ The price of the apple is   20 minutes.

☐ Mom went to sharpen   a slice of pizza.

☐ Dad went to wash   a pencil.

☐ Cedric sat on the fence, eating   his face.

→ Put an X next to the correct answer.

Who had the biggest helping of cereal for breakfast?

_____ (a) Celeste's bowl of cereal was $\frac{1}{4}$ empty.

_____ (b) Camika's bowl of cereal was $\frac{1}{2}$ empty.

_____ (c) Cesar's bowl of cereal was $\frac{1}{2}$ full.

Which would be the fastest?

_____ (a) a jet whose trip has been canceled

_____ (b) a spaceship that has run out of fuel

_____ (c) a tortoise descending a hill

Which would be the loudest?

_____ (a) a DVD player that is not plugged in

_____ (b) a bird chirping on the fence in the yard

_____ (c) a singer who has lost his voice

Who would be the happiest?

_____ (a) Grace has a slice of stone with concrete sauce.

_____ (b) Caleb has stale rice that has become hard.

_____ (c) Tracey has orange juice with an ice cube.

Celia the Centipede

How many legs do you think a centipede has?

(a) about 100   (b) about 30   (c) about 2 or 3

 Read the story to find out. Then answer the questions.

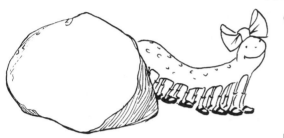

Hi. Let me introduce myself. I am Celia the Centipede. Welcome to my home under this rock. I hope you don't find it too damp, but we centipedes like moist places. My sisters have decided to move to a pile of leaves because they say it's more peaceful. But this rock reminds me of the huge stone buildings in the city and, you must admit, it's nice and cool.

Why am I called a centipede? you ask. The word **"centipede"** means one hundred legs. I may look like I have a hundred legs, but I don't. I'm not certain, but I think I have about 30. I am made of many segments, or parts, and I have one pair of legs on each segment. I also have a pair of poison claws under my mouth that I use to kill prey. So watch out (just kidding).

I think we centipedes are very graceful when we move. This is because our hinge-like joints let us move smoothly over the ground.

I don't eat fancy food like you folks. But I am a meat-eater and, I must say, I do like a nice juicy snail, slug, or worm. They really are excellent eaten raw.

And with that advice, Celia the Centipede disappeared into the recess under a rock.

"Do you need shoes for *all* feet?"

➔ What did you learn about centipedes? Circle the correct answer.

1. Centipedes like to live in

    (a) dry places.   (b) moist places.

2. The word "centipede" means

    (a) a hundred legs.   (b) a thousand legs.

3. Centipedes have about

    (a) 56 legs.   (b) 30 legs.

4. The centipede's poison claws are

    (a) under its mouth.   (b) under its last segment.

5. The centipede has

    (a) hinge-like joints.   (b) stiff joints.

6. The centipede eats

    (a) only plants.   (b) meat.

7. In the last sentence, Celia disappears into the recess under the rock. Which definition of the word recess does Celia mean?

    (a) to stop work; to take a break   (b) a hidden inner place

➔ Reread the story and underline all the words that have the **s** sound for **c**. Include the title and count each word, even if it comes more than once. See if you can find all 23.

Cynthia's Pen Pal

Cynthia has a pen pal. Her name is Cicely. Can you guess where Cicely comes from? These mini-jokes will give you the answer:

Q: Where were the first French fries made?

A: In Greece.

Q: What did the American say when he saw the writing on the building?

A: It's all Greek to me.

 Read this letter from Cynthia's pen pal Cicely.

Hi Cynthia,

Thank you for your recent letter telling me about America. I showed it to my classmates at recess. We think your city, Cincinnati, looks like a nice place.

Since you asked me, I wanted to let you know I am happy to help you with your Greek history project. It sounds like fun.

I am proud of my Greek history. It goes back 2,500 years. That is twenty-five centuries. Back then Greece was the center of the Western world. It was the place where everyone came to trade and meet.

We still have buildings from long ago. Most of them have been in ruins for a long time. From looking at the ruins, you would not realize how advanced my **ancestors** really were. They built huge, well-balanced buildings with graceful columns to honor their gods. They also built very large arenas for plays and homes that had excellent plumbing.

The Greeks were very **civilized**. They had great respect for each other. This led to their unique form of government. For the first time the **citizens** had a voice in the **policy** of the government. They could state their opinions, vote, and serve in every level of government—that is, as long as they were men. But I am proud that **democracy** was born in Greece.

→ Checking up: See if you are following the letter. Circle the correct answer.

1. Cynthia lives in

    (a) Columbus.

    (b) Cincinnati.

2. Cicely lives in

    (a) Greece.

    (b) Egypt.

3. Greece was the center of the Western world

    (a) 1,000 years ago.

    (b) 2,500 years ago.

4. The Greeks built huge buildings

    (a) to honor their gods.

    (b) to attend concerts.

5. Which is correct?

    (a) Every citizen had a voice in the policy of the government.

    (b) Only men had a voice in the policy of the government.

6. Which is correct?

    (a) The Greeks invented a new form of government.

    (b) The Greeks copied the Egyptian form of government.

 Now read the next page of Cicely's letter.

The Greeks decided to create new laws. The laws were unusual because they were for everyone, not just the leaders and rulers. Also, the laws were created by the citizens and could not be changed without their agreement.

*What I admire most about my ancestors is that they tried to do everything as well as they could. They strived for **excellence**. You see this in their buildings, sculptures, and other kinds of art. You also see it in the Olympic Games, which they started in 776 B.C. The winners of the races received no prizes, but they were admired because they had excelled.*

The Olympic Games were held in honor of the god Zeus. The Greeks had many gods who were important in their lives. They saw the gods as like humans in many ways, and they wrote many stories about them.

The Greeks were interested in finding out about new things, and they made huge advances in science, medicine, math, and engineering. We can trace many of our advances today back to the discoveries they made.

I am proud of what my ancestors did. And I am glad that I live in Greece. It is like living in the past and the present at the same time. When I sit in the colossal arena of my hometown, Athens, I can almost see and hear my ancestors as they watch one of their Greek plays. History surrounds me every day. I hope this letter will help you with your project. Good luck. Let me know how you do.

Sincerely,

Cicely

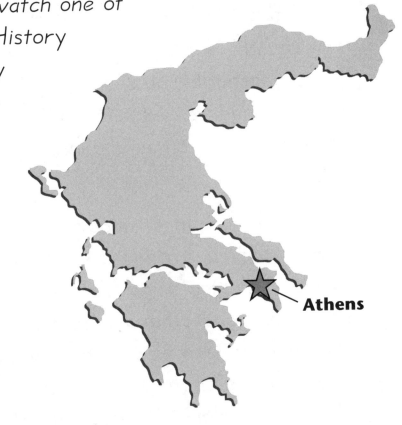

Athens

➜ Circle the correct answer.

1. The Greek laws were

    (a) created by the leaders.

    (b) created by the citizens.

2. Cicely admired her ancestors most for their

    (a) desire for excellence.

    (b) love of games.

3. The Olympic Games were

    (a) a chance to complete and win prizes.

    (b) in honor of the god Zeus.

4. The Greeks made huge advances in

    (a) science.

    (b) space travel.

6. Cicely enjoys living in Greece because

    (a) it is like living in the past and the present at the same time.

    (b) it is like living in the present and the future at the same time.

➜ Match the words with their meanings.

_____	1. ancestors	(a) people who live in a city or town and have the right to vote
_____	2. civilized	(b) family members who lived before you
_____	3. citizens	(c) having a well-developed culture with education, art, science, and government

_____ 1. policy   (a) form of government in which the citizens choose their leaders

_____ 2. democracy   (b) a plan or rule

_____ 3. excellence   (c) the quality or state of being extremely good; first class

→ Use the words below to complete the sentences on the chalkboard of a class at the Celina School.

ancestors   excellence   civilized   policy   democracy   Citizens

1. The school _____ is no food in the classroom.

2. The history project is to try to trace your _____ .

3. Please behave in a _____ way during the speaker's visit.

4. _____ of our town will be voting tomorrow at the Celina School.

5. Always strive for _____ in your work.

6. Ms. Centinelli told us that this class is not run as a _____ and that she has the final say.

▲ Challenge

Did you notice the incorrect spelling in the answer to the first mini-joke on p. 19?

The word meaning "fat used to cook" should be spelled _____.

When two words like *Greece* and *grease* sound the same but have different spellings and different meanings, they are called **homophones.**

The Greeks wanted to excel in their activities. Write about what you would like to do well in, and why. You can write about any activity you wish—a sport, a subject at school, a hobby—or something that you like to do.

_____

_____

_____

_____

_____

_____

_____

_____

_____

_____

_____

_____

Ph has the **f** sound.

phone

trophy

Sound out the letters to read each word.

photo	phonics	nephew	graph
pharmacy	orphan	dolphin	hyphen
elephant	pamphlet	phrase	typhoon

alphabet   autograph   paragraph   biography

geography   emphasis   physical   autobiography

→ Find a word from the lists above to answer the riddles. Write the word on the line.

1. I have aunts and uncles: _____

2. You go to me to get medicine: _____

3. A group of words with no verb: _____

4. A book about someone: _____

5. When you ask a famous person to write her name for you, she gives you this: _____

6. It is made up of sentences: _____

7. In this class you study about the planet we live on: _____

8. A very powerful storm: _____

➜ Circle the name of the picture.

typhoon hyphen	emphasis alphabet	Phyllis Philip
orphan graph	dolphin elephant	phonics photo

➜ Read the sentence and circle the correct word.

1. Sophie got out her (graph, dolphin) paper to do her math homework.

2. Joseph wrote three (elephants, paragraphs) for his writing assignment.

3. Ralph read about (phonics, typhoons) for geography class.

4. Phoebe and Josephine practiced throwing and catching for (physics, physical) education.

5. Stephen took (nephews, photos) of Phoebe and Josephine for the school newspaper.

6. Ms. Phineas sorted out her plastic (alphabet, autograph) letters to get ready for her phonics lesson.

→ Put an X in the box next to the sentence that tells about the picture.

☐ Philippa phoned her Dad to say she would be late.

☐ Uncle Raphael met his nephew at the bus stop.

☐ The photographer took a photo of the typhoon.

☐ The typhoon blew the leaves off the tree.

☐ Phaela won the geography quiz.

☐ Stephan won a trophy for physical fitness.

☐ Ms. Philips wrote a paragraph on the board.

☐ Mr. Clephans wrote the alphabet on the board.

→ Find a word from the list below to complete each sentence. Then write the word on the line.

Graph   dolphin   alphabet   biography

1. The _____ is made up of vowels and consonants.

2. _____ paper is useful for doing math.

3. Ophelia was reading a _____ of Martin Luther King Jr.

4. The _____ gracefully jumped out of the water.

pharmacist   physically   autobiography   elephant

5. An _____ is when you write about yourself.

6. Everyone watched the _____ eating peanuts with its long trunk.

7. Gym classes keep you _____ fit.

8. A _____ prepares medicines.

Zoo Assistant Wanted

 Phyllis saw this ad in the paper and was excited. Read the story to find out why.

> # Zoo assistant wanted. Part time. After-school hours. Must love animals.

Phyllis loved animals and knew she would enjoy working at the zoo. She quickly sat down and wrote a short autobiography of herself. It was two paragraphs long. It described her physical features, her grades (A in geography), and her hobbies, which included photography. She then emphasized her interest in animals, explaining that she had a dog and two gophers.

She added a photograph of herself and mailed everything. She hoped she would get the job.

➜ Circle the correct answer.

1. The ad was for a job at

    (a) the pharmacy.   (b) the zoo.

2. Phyllis wrote

    (a) two phrases.   (b) two paragraphs.

3. Phyllis got an A in

    (a) geography.   (b) physical education.

4. Phyllis has

    (a) an elephant.   (b) gophers.

5. Phyllis also sent

    (a) a photograph.   (b) a telegraph.

Reread the story and underline all the **ph** words. There are 9.

Ph Words:
Pharaoh (fā'-rō)

> **Why do you think the pyramids were built? Circle the correct answer. They were**

(a) palaces for the kings to live in.

(b) theaters with stages for plays.

(c) tombs for the kings with hidden passages.

 Read the passage to find out what this **ph** word means.

The funeral barges made their way up the Nile River toward the Great Pyramid of Khufu. Like other pharoahs, when Khufu became the ruler of Egypt, he began planning a pyramid that would be his tomb. Now, 23 years later, this huge structure was ready for its king.

This day was of great importance to the Egyptians because the pharaoh was both their god and their king. He was their ruler in every sense of the word. He owned the land and controlled every part of the Egyptians' lives.

➔ Circle the correct answer.

Pharaoh means

(a) a builder of pyramids.　　(b) a ruler or king.

Metamorphosis (met-ə-mor′-fə-sis)

> **How does a caterpillar grow into a butterfly?**

 Read the passage to find out what this **ph** word means.

Most insects make a complete change during their lives. The change involves four stages and is called *metamorphosis.* That is a long word for such tiny beings! The four stages are egg, larva, pupa, and adult.

When the egg hatches, the larva comes out. It looks like a worm. The larva of a moth or a butterfly is a caterpillar.

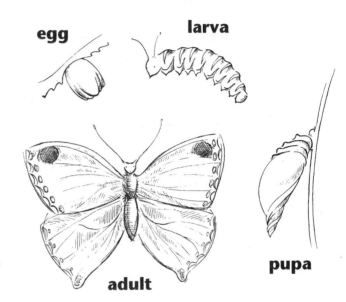

The larva eats a lot and grows quickly. When it is fully grown, the larva finds a sheltered spot and spins a protective covering, or cocoon. This is the pupa stage. Much happens inside the cocoon. The legs and wings grow. Cells develop into an adult that is very different from the caterpillar. When metamorphosis is complete, the cocoon splits open and a beautiful moth or butterfly comes out.

➜ Circle the correct answer.

Metamorphosis

    (a) is the change that insects go through as they develop into adults.

    (b) explains how butterflies become the parents of a caterpillar.

"Was that really me?"

Amphibians (am-fib′-ē-ns)

> **How are butterflies and frogs similar? How does a tadpole become a frog?**

 Read the passage to find out what this **ph** word means.

Frogs, like butterflies, change physically during their life. Like butterflies, they go through metamorphosis.

Frogs begin life as tadpoles. They come out of soft, jelly-covered eggs, looking like fish with long tails.

Gradually, tadpoles grow legs. They develop lungs and a mouth. Their eyes get bigger and their insides shrink. Finally, after about two months, the tail shrinks, and they look like frogs because they are frogs now!

Frogs, like toads, are amphibians. Amphibians are cold-blooded animals with a backbone, and they can live both on land and in water. Frogs begin life in the water when they are tadpoles, but they prefer to live on land when they are adults—as long as their skin is kept moist.

Amphibians are important because they eat insects and other pests. Unfortunately, the number of amphibians is decreasing worldwide. One reason is because their habitats—the forests, rivers, and marshes where they live—are being destroyed. They are also taken from their habitats to be sold as pets and for food.

➔ Circle the correct answer.

Amphibians

    (a) live both on land and in water.

    (b) have no backbone.

Physics (fiz'-iks)

Why does a ball fall down to the ground?

 Read the passage to find out what this **ph** word means.

You miss the ball and it falls to the ground. Your birthday balloon slips out of your hand and floats away. On a hot day, your ice cream melts before you have time to finish it. Why do these things happen?

The science of physics gives us the answers. Physics is a science that seeks the reasons for how things work. People in physics study matter, which is what all things are made of. Physicists also study movement, force, and forms of energy such as heat and electricity.

➜ Circle the correct answer.

Physics

    (a) makes balls fall to the ground, balloons float away, and ice cream melt.

    (b) explains why balls fall to the ground, balloons float away, and ice cream melts.

Physics helps us understand why volcanoes erupt.

The Story of Persephone

Many places have winter for part of the year, a time when it is cold and green plants and grass stop growing. What is the reason this Greek myth, or story, gives for why there is winter?

 Read the story to find out.

Persephone (Pǝr-se'-fǝ-nē) was once happy and carefree. Her mother, Demeter (Di-mē'-tǝr), who was the goddess of the harvest, loved her dearly. Demeter always took Persephone with her as she looked after the trees and flowers.

One day Persephone was gathering flowers in the meadow. Suddenly, the ground opened up and a chariot pulled by black horses appeared. In the chariot was Hades, the god of the underworld. He grabbed Persephone and returned down, down, down to the underworld.

Demeter came looking for Persephone, but she could not find her. She was desperate. Tears of sorrow fell from her eyes. At the same time, the leaves of the trees and the petals from the flowers dropped to the ground. All nature was sad along with Demeter, and everything stopped growing.

Demeter continued to look for Persephone, but no one knew where she was. At last she came to Helios, the sun. He had seen Hades snatch Persephone away.

"She is with Hades. She is now in the underworld," said Helios.

Demeter was so angry that she went to Zeus, the greatest of the gods. She said she would never let the land become green again or let the flowers grow until she got back Persephone.

→ Checking up: See if you are following the story. Circle the correct answer:

1. Persephone's mother Demeter was

   (a) the goddess of song.

   (b) the goddess of the harvest.

2. When Hades captured Persephone, she was

   (a) sitting by the river.

   (b) picking flowers.

3. Hades appeared

   (a) out of the ground.

   (b) from behind a tree.

4. When tears fell from Demeter's eyes,

   (a) the sky cried tears of rain.

   (b) the leaves of the trees and the petals of the flowers fell to the ground.

5. The one who knew where Persephone could be found was

   (a) Helios, the sun.

   (b) Zeus, the greatest of the gods.

6. What do you think happens next in the story?

   (a) Demeter digs a big hole in the ground to reach Persephone.

   (b) Zeus says he will help Demeter get back Persephone.

Zeus sent Hermes, the messenger of the gods, to tell Hades that he must let Persephone go. But when Hermes arrived, he saw that Persephone had eaten some pomegranate seeds.

"Oh, no! It is too late," he cried.

Persephone, who was excited to see Hermes, asked: "What do you mean, it's too late?"

"You have eaten food that belonged to Hades. This means you can never leave the underworld. You must stay here forever." He emphasized the word "forever."

Persephone burst into tears. She was longing to go home to her dear mother.

Unhappy to see Persephone so upset, Hermes took Persephone's hand.

"I will go back to Zeus," he said, "He will decide what should be done."

Zeus considered the matter carefully. Then he declared: "Demeter and Persephone should not be parted forever. But, because Persephone ate six pomegranate seeds, she must return to the underworld for six months of every year."

So, every year, Persephone leaves Demeter and returns to the underworld. Then Demeter is sad. Nothing grows in nature and there is winter. But Persephone always comes back in the spring. And all the trees and flowers become green and bloom again.

➜ Circle the correct answer.

1. To get Persephone back

    (a) Zeus went down into the underworld to tell Hades to let Persephone go.

    (b) Zeus sent Hermes to the underworld to tell Hades to let Persephone go.

2. Hermes said it was too late because

    (a) Persephone had eaten some pomegranate seeds.

    (b) Persephone now liked living in the underworld.

3. Who decided Persephone should return to the underworld every year?

    (a) Hermes

    (b) Zeus

4. A pomegranate is

    (a) a fruit.

    (b) a drink.

5. How many pomegranate seeds did Persephone eat?

    (a) four

    (b) six

6. In the story, winter came for six months each year because

    (a) Hades would not let anything grow in nature when Persephone returned to her mother.

    (b) Demeter was sad and nothing could grow in nature when Persephone returned to the underworld.

Both the caterpillar and the tadpole change into different beings. What, or who, would you like to change into, and why would you like to be that thing or being?

_____

_____

_____

_____

_____

_____

_____

_____

_____

_____

_____

_____

_____

_____

_____

Sometimes letters have **no** sound.

comb

knee

Sound out the letters to reach each word.

t	often	listen	fasten	soften
k	know	knee	knob	knock
w	write	wrap	wrong	whole
h	hour	honest	rhyme	honor
l	half	yolk	calm	folk
b	climb	thumb	lamb	crumb

wrist	knew	wrote	comb
knot	palm	wreck	knife
wring	calf	rhythm	numb
hasten	glisten	dumb	wrestle

Learn to read these words: high night

➔ Match the words with their meanings.

often	hurry	glisten	having the same sound
wrong	frequently	rhyme	pattern of accents and beats
hasten	incorrect	rhythm	to shine

→ Read the words and draw a slash mark (\ ) through the silent letters.
Then match the words that have the same silent letters.

fasten	know	calm	wring
knot	honor	wrote	yolk
hour	often	lamb	comb
rhyme	wreck	glisten	half
climb	crumb	whole	hasten
wrap	honest	palm	wrong

→ Circle the name of the picture.

fasten / soften / listen	know / knee / knob	wrap / write / wrist
honest / honor / hour	folk / yolk / half	thumb / crumbs / lamb

→ Circle the missing letter in each sentence. Then write the letter on the line to complete the word.

1. Two halves make a ___hole.   l   t   w

2. An ___our is made up of sixty minutes.   b   h   k

3. Pa___m trees grow only in tropical climates.   t   w   l

4. Lam___s are baby sheep.   h   b   t

5. Ca___ves are baby cows.   b   w   l

6. Your calf can be found below your ___nee.   w   k   h

7. The yellow part of an egg is the yo___k.   l   t   k

8. Poetry often has r___yming words.   k   l   h

The Deserted House

→ Read the story and write the missing words on the lines.

crumbling   **answered**   **knob**   **John**

hour   **half**   **knocked**   **dumb**

The house looked bleak and lonely in the _____ dark. It

was _____ into ruins because no one had cared for it for

so long.

_____ had always wanted to look inside. But now he was

afraid. He stood there for half an _____. Then he said to

himself, "This is _____. There's nothing to be afraid of."

He _____ on the door, but naturally no one

_____. He slowly turned the _____ and

pushed open the door.

listened   **wrong**   **palms**   **whole**

calm   **knew**   **rhythmic**   **glistening**

As soon as John got inside, he _____ that something was

_____ . Everything was clean and _____ .

He _____ and remained still. A _____

sound came from a back room.

Slowly, the door to that room began to open. The _____ of

John's hands became sweaty and his _____ body began to

shake with fear.

"I must keep _____ ," he said to himself. He waited. What

happened next?

What do you think is going to happen next? Think about the ending that
you would like. Then write the ending on page 55.

→ Reread the story to be sure that the words you have added make sense. Then answer the questions.

Circle the correct answer.

1. John visited the house

    (a) in the afternoon.   (b) in the evening.

2. The word bleak means

    (a) beautiful.   (b) gloomy, not cheerful.

3. The door was

    (a) locked.   (b) unlocked.

4. Everything inside was

    (a) dusty and dirty.   (b) clean and glistening.

5. John was

    (a) afraid.   (b) cheerful.

6. Do you think this story is true?

    (a) yes   (b) no

→ Put an X on the line next to the sentence that tells what each saying means.

1. Rome was not built in a day.

_____ (a) Rome was built at night.

_____ (b) Rome is still being built.

_____ (c) It took a long time to build Rome.

2. When in Rome, do as the Romans do.

_____ (a) When in Rome, be sure to speak Italian.

_____ (b) Follow the customs of the place you are visiting.

_____ (c) When someone tells you to do something, you should do it.

Rome

What is Rome? Circle what you think it is.

   (a) a monument

   (b) a palace

   (c) a city

 Read the story to find out how the city of Rome began.

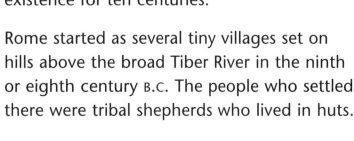

Rome is the capital of Italy. Like Greece, it has many ruins of buildings that have been there for thousands of years. Rome has been in existence for ten centuries.

Rome started as several tiny villages set on hills above the broad Tiber River in the ninth or eighth century B.C. The people who settled there were tribal shepherds who lived in huts.

They would be amazed to know that their tiny, quiet villages were to become the center of a far-reaching empire, the most powerful and largest empire in the world.

This is what happened. Over time, the villagers came down from the hills and formed a city. They surrounded it with strong walls, built many buildings, and made the city a center for trade and government.

Then came invasions (in-vā-zhəns) and other disasters such as a great fire and an earthquake. Rome went through periods of highs and lows. Between the lows came times of great progress in building, government, and culture. The buildings became spectacular; huge monuments and paved roads were constructed. Romans built aqueducts, which are pipes for carrying water.

Meanwhile, the Romans moved into new areas and conquered lands as far away as England. And as they went, they spread their culture. They also spread ideas they had learned from the Greeks.

Yes, the shepherds who quietly tended their sheep on the hills overlooking Rome would not have recognized the empire that developed in the place they once called home.

→ Circle the correct answer.

1. Rome is the capital of

    (a) Greece.

    (b) Italy.

2. Rome started as tiny villages

    (a) on hills above the Tiber River.

    (b) next to the Tiber River.

3. The early Romans protected their new city by

    (a) surrounding it with a strong wall.

    (b) building strong forts.

4. Rome was hurt by

    (a) tornadoes.

    (b) a great fire.

5. An aqueduct is

    (a) a paved roadway.

    (b) pipes that carry water.

6. The Romans

    (a) conquered many lands.

    (b) conquered only the Greeks.

➡ Learn to read these words with the silent letters **gh**. Look for these words in the next story.

brought	caught	right
thought	daughter	straight

➡ Choose one of the words from the list above to complete each sentence.

1. Mr. Johnson went shopping with his ———————————— , Sarah.

2. Sarah ———————————— she needed a new baseball cap because she had been chosen for the school team.

3. They went ————————————to the sports store.

4. Sarah tried on several caps but none of them looked or felt ————————————.

5. Then a cool red cap ————————————her eye.

6. Sarah tried on the red cap and it was perfect, so she bought it and ———————————— it home.

Romulus and Remus

> **Which twin do you think created the city of Rome?**

    (a) Romulus   (b) Remus

You have read a factual account about the beginning of Rome. Here is a Roman legend, or story, that tells how the city came into being.

The sun was shining, the sky was blue, and all was calm. Gently floating down the River Tiber was a basket. As the basket bobbed up and down rhythmically, something moved inside.

As night fell, the basket became **caught** in some grassy plants on the bank of the river. An hour later, in the half dark, a creature appeared. It climbed down the high riverbank. Every now and then, it stopped to listen. It was a wolf looking for her lost babies.

The wolf peered into the basket. There, wrapped in a beautiful cloak fastened by a glistening pin, were tiny twin boys. One was happily sucking his thumb. One was softly gurgling to himself.

The wolf gently lifted the babies by clasping the cloak in her teeth. Then she carried them **straight** back to her den. There she warmed them with her body and fed them with her milk.

The wolf looked after the boys for nine months. Then, one day, a shepherd found the boys playing happily in the wolf's den. He was amazed. He wrapped them in their cloak and **brought** them home to his wife.

At the sight of the boys, his wife began to shake with fear.

"What is the matter?" her husband asked.

"You must take them away. Look at the cloak, it has the letter *N* for *Numitor,* who used to be king. These boys must be his grandsons. If King Amulius finds out that we have them, he will be angry with us."

She was right. Amulius hated his older brother Numitor and his family. He had taken away the throne from Numitor, and he did not want him, or any of his family, to regain it.

The shepherd was calm.

"It will be fine. We will tell no one. We will bring them up as our own sons," he said.

And that is what they did.

→ Checking up: See if you are following the story. Circle the correct answer.

1. What was floating down the River Tiber?

    (a) a basket

    (b) a box

2. What was the wolf looking for?

    (a) food

    (b) her babies

3. What were the twins wrapped in?

    (a) a colorful blanket

    (b) a beautiful cloak

4. How long did the wolf look after the twin boys?

    (a) nine months

    (b) nine years

5. Who found the boys in the wolf's den?

    (a) a woodcutter

    (b) a shepherd

6. Why was the shepherd's wife afraid?

    (a) She did not know how to look after the boys.

    (b) She knew the boys were the grandsons of Numitor, who used to be king.

7. What did the shepherd say they would do?

    (a) take the boys back to the wolf

    (b) bring them up as their own sons

 Years went by. Romulus and Remus grew strong and handsome. They helped on the farm, which belonged to King Amulius. They did not know that their grandfather, Numitor, lived on the next farm.

One day Romulus and Remus got into an argument with the shepherds on Numitor's farm. They were **brought** before Numitor.

Numitor was impressed with the two handsome young men who spoke so well and walked with kingly bearing.

Then he had another surprise. The shepherd **thought** that Numitor would hurt the boys, so he ran in and cried, "Numitor, spare these boys. They are your **daughter's** children."

Numitor listened to the shepherd's story. His eyes glistened with tears of happiness as he hugged the twins.

Romulus and Remus also were overjoyed that Numitor was their grandfather. They vowed that they would defeat Amulius and return Numitor to the throne. They **sought** out Amulius and did this.

Later, the twins decided that they would build a new city to celebrate. It was to be on one of the seven hills that rose up on both sides of the River Tiber.

They could not decide which hill to build the city on.

They climbed one hill, and Romulus said, "Let's build the city **right** here."

But Remus said, "No, let's build it on that one," and he pointed to another hill.

Romulus and Remus argued and argued and became very angry at each other. They came to blows.

Romulus overpowered his brother and he became the king of the new city.

Romulus named the city after himself. Rome became the capital of Italy and it continues to thrive today, two thousand years later.

→ Circle the correct answer.

1. Romulus and Remus worked

(a) in the house of Amulius.

(b) on the farm of Amulius.

2. Numitor found his grandsons because

(a) the shepherd explained what had happened.

(b) the twins guessed he was their grandfather.

3. Did the twins return Numitor to the throne as they promised?

(a) yes

(b) no

4. The twins argued because

(a) they could not decide what to name the new city.

(b) they wanted to build the city on different hills.

5. Who got to name the city?

(a) Romulus

(b) Remus

6. Today, Rome is

    (a) in ruins.

    (b) the capital of Italy.

✎ Write your ending to the story, "The Deserted House." You may want to reread the story on page 44 before you begin.

_____

_____

_____

_____

_____

_____

_____

_____

_____

_____

_____

_____

_____

_____

_____

Lesson 5: Syllables

To read a long word, break it into **syllables.** A word has as many syllables as it has **vowel sounds.**

1. page
2. dol-phin
3. glis-ten-ing
4. bi-og-ra-phy

Remember: There is only one vowel sound when there is a **silent e,** as in *age*, and when two vowels come together and the **first** one is **long** and the **second** one is **silent**, as in *know*.

→ Circle the vowels. Write the number of vowels in each word. Then write the number of vowel sounds and syllables in the word.

	Vowels	Vowel Sounds and Syllables		Vowels	Vowel Sounds and Syllables
often	_____	_____	typhoon	_____	_____
graph	_____	_____	concert	_____	_____
gym	_____	_____	knee	_____	_____
recent	_____	_____	certain	_____	_____
margin	_____	_____	judge	_____	_____
phonics	_____	_____	physical	_____	_____
icy	_____	_____	energy	_____	_____
giant	_____	_____	knew	_____	_____
alphabet	_____	_____	paragraph	_____	_____
message	_____	_____	legend	_____	_____
honor	_____	_____	Pacific	_____	_____
geography	_____	_____	elephant	_____	_____
edge	_____	_____	ginger	_____	_____
rhyme	_____	_____	page	_____	_____
emphasis	_____	_____	graceful	_____	_____

➔ Draw a line between the words that have the same number of syllables.

ice   dolphin   cereal   margin

honor   gem   alphabet   honest

nephew   city   wrist   recess

large   whole   phonics   bridge

giant   glisten   stage   photo

geography   physically   wringing   dance

➔ Draw a line between the beginning and the end of each word.

sof	age	hy	ic	mar	ew
pass	cent	mag	phen	rhym	ing
pho	ten	de	est	neph	ter
re	to	hon	cide	cen	gin

→ Study the map of Africa on the opposite page. It gives you information you need to know before you read the next passage.

Find the following on the map. Circle each one:

1. North, South, East, and West

2. Europe, Africa, and Asia

3. the equator

4. the Nile River and the Congo River
   Circle the X at the mouth of the river (where it flows into the sea).

5. Vertical and horizontal

6. Match the words with their meanings.

    vertical   across
    horizontal   up and down

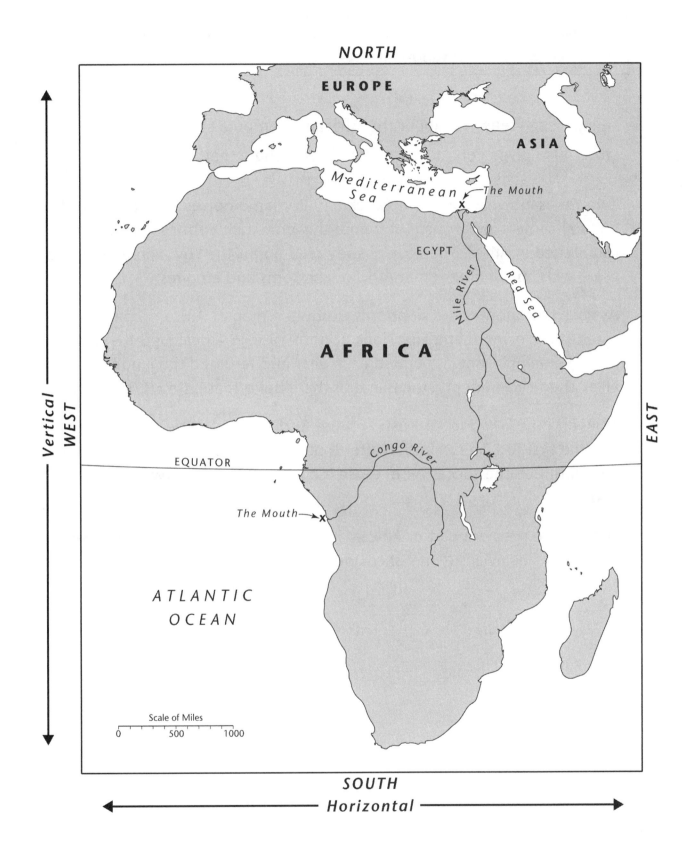

NORTH

EUROPE

ASIA

Mediterranean
Sea

The Mouth

X

EGYPT

Nile River

Red Sea

AFRICA

Congo River

EQUATOR

The Mouth ⟶ X

ATLANTIC
OCEAN

Vertical
WEST

EAST

Scale of Miles
0   500   1000

SOUTH
Horizontal

Africa

**What kingdoms came before the Greek and Roman empires?
Where are they on the map?**

 This passage tells you about the African kingdoms and empires of long ago. It also gives you more practice in reading a map.

Two thousand years ago, the Greek and Roman **empires** became powerful cultural centers in Europe. But before this time, rich **cultures** had been established in Africa. You have already read about the Egyptian empire, but there were many other great African kingdoms and empires.

As you read about these kingdoms, study the map of Africa on page 63 carefully to locate them. First, look at northeastern Africa. Find the giant Nile River. Remember how it flooded each year and fertilized the land? Circle the Nile. Then circle **Egypt**—the name of the empire that lasted 3,000 years.

Now find the kingdom of **Kush** and the **Red Sea** and circle them. Kush was the first African civilization after that of the Egyptians. Here the Axum Kingdom became successful because it controlled trade between Africa and Asia.

Look at the northern part of Africa. Find **Carthage**. Circle it. This is where the seafaring Phoenicians (Fi-nē'-shəns) founded a kingdom way back in 750 B.C.

→ Checking up: See if you are following the passage. Circle the correct answer.

1. Some African kingdoms and empires were established before the Greek and Roman empires.

    (a) yes

    (b) no

2. The Nile River is in

    (a) southwestern Africa.

    (b) northeastern Africa.

3. Kush is near

    (a) the Red Sea.

    (b) the Mediterranean Sea.

4. The Axum Kingdom controlled trade between

    (a) Africa and Asia.

    (b) Africa and Europe.

5. The Phoenicians founded a kingdom in

    (a) the southern part of Africa.

    (b) the northern part of Africa.

6. The Phoenicians were

    (a) seafaring people.

    (b) farmers.

Find **Ghana** on the map on page 63. Circle it. This is where the first West African Kingdom developed. It grew rich from its gold mines.

Find **Mali**. Circle it. The Malis overcame the Ghanians and built a trading empire that stretched across the huge Sahara Desert. Which animals do you think carried goods across the dry desert? Yes, camels. Circle the **Sahara Desert.**

The Malis were eventually overcome by the **Songhai**. Find Songhai and circle it.

Another powerful group of people were the Bantus. They settled at the mouth of the **Congo River**. Put an X at the mouth of the Congo River. They also settled in Zimbabwe where they found gold. Circle **Zimbabwe**. Here they built cities with great stone palaces for their kings. The largest palace is still there. It is called the "Great Zimbabwe."

Although these great African kingdoms and empires no longer exist, their rich **heritage** has been passed on to us.

➔ Match the words with their meanings.

_____ 1. culture

(a) something passed on from one's ancestors or the past

_____ 2. empire

(b) the beliefs, art, and ways of behaving of a group of people

_____ 3. heritage

(c) a large amount of land or number of people under the control of one government or ruler

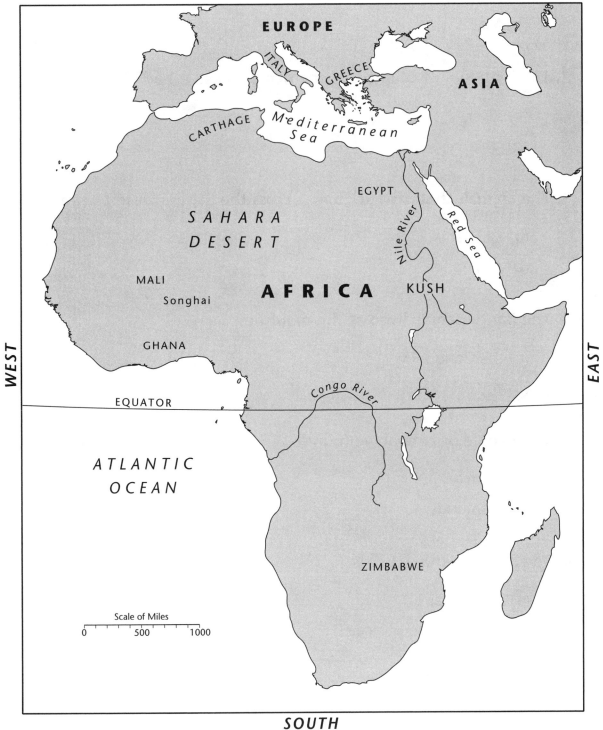

NORTH

EUROPE

ITALY

GREECE

ASIA

CARTHAGE

Mediterranean
Sea

EGYPT

SAHARA
DESERT

Nile River

Red Sea

MALI

AFRICA

KUSH

Songhai

GHANA

WEST

EAST

Congo River

EQUATOR

ATLANTIC
OCEAN

ZIMBABWE

Scale of Miles

0   500   1000

SOUTH

→ Circle the correct answer.

1. The first kingdom to develop in West Africa was

(a) Ghana.

(b) Mali.

2. The Kingdom of Ghana became rich because it had

(a) silver.

(b) gold.

3. The animals that carried goods across the Sahara Desert were

(a) elephants.

(b) camels.

4. The Bantu people lived at the mouth of

(a) the Congo River.

(b) the Nile River.

5. The people of Zimbabwe found

(a) gold.

(b) diamonds.

6. The "Great Zimbabwe" is

(a) a mountain.

(b) a large stone palace.

How Rabbit Tricked Elephant and Whale: An African Folktale

> **How did Rabbit trick Elephant and Whale, two friends who thought they were too big and important to bother with her?**

(a) by having a race   (b) by having a tug-of-war

 Read this African folktale to find out.

It was a beautiful day, just the sort of day that made Rabbit glad that she lived in Africa.

She hopped along in a graceful rhythm, happily singing, "Africa's a nice place to be, a nice place to be."

She had not gone far when she saw Giraffe, who was peacefully nibbling the high treetops.

"Nice day, don't you think?" asked Rabbit.

"It's always a nice day. You seem to have a lot of energy today," replied Giraffe. She went on munching and Rabbit went on hopping and singing.

Next, Rabbit came upon a wide, open space where Elephant was standing in the sun.

"Nice day, don't you think?" asked Rabbit.

Elephant raised her trunk. Barely glancing at Rabbit, she snorted, "Go away, Rabbit. I don't have time to waste on someone your size."

Now, Rabbit was a peace-loving Rabbit, but she did not like being spoken to like that.

"You may be the giant of animals, but there's no need to be rude," said Rabbit.

But Elephant took no notice of her.

Anger welled up in Rabbit. But, instead of going off in a rage, she calmly left.

She made her way out of the tropical forest and climbed the cliff. She sat on the edge of the cliff looking out at the sea, thinking.

She saw Whale in the distance. She decided to ask her about Elephant's rudeness.

"Hey, Whale," she yelled in her loudest voice. "Hey, Whale, come here."

Whale swam over to see who was calling her. At first she did not spot Rabbit. Then she spied the little animal at the top of the cliff.

"Rabbit, was that you yelling at me?" Whale asked, irritably.

"Yes," answered Rabbit.

"Why do you think I would want to say anything to you? You're far too tiny and weak to be of interest to me."

And with that she turned around and swam away.

Rabbit watched her leave. But she smiled. She had an idea.

➔ Checking up: See if you are following the story. Circle the correct answer.

1. The story comes from

    (a) Italy.

    (b) Africa.

2. When Rabbit started the day, she was

    (a) happy.

    (b) sad.

3. The first animal Rabbit met was

   (a) Giraffe.

   (b) Elephant.

4. Elephant would not speak to Rabbit because

   (a) she talked too much.

   (b) she was too little to bother with.

5. Rabbit left Elephant

   (a) angrily.

   (b) calmly.

6. Rabbit sat thinking

   (a) on the edge of a cliff.

   (b) in a wide-open space.

7. Whale

   (a) did not come to Rabbit when she yelled at her.

   (b) did not want to say anything to her.

 What do you think Rabbit's idea was? Read on.

Rabbit shouted to Whale, "Listen, Whale. You have it wrong. I may be tiny, but I am not weak. In fact, I am stronger than you. I could beat you at a tug-of-war."

Whale nearly choked from laughing.

"That's the dumbest idea. But fine. Get a rope and we'll see who is stronger," she replied.

Rabbit found the thickest and strongest vine. Then she went straight to Elephant.

"Elephant, you were very rude to me today. I want you to know that I am just as good as you are and just as strong."

Elephant smiled as she wrapped her trunk around a tasty branch.

"And how might you show that?" she asked, amused.

"I will beat you at a tug-of-war," declared Rabbit.

"Do I have this right? You will beat me at a tug-of-war?" laughed Elephant.

"Yes," said Rabbit firmly.

"Oh, all right. Anything for peace and quiet," said Elephant, and she fastened the vine around her huge, wide waist.

"Don't tug until I tell you to," said Rabbit.

Rabbit then raced back to Whale with the other end of the vine.

"Tie this to your tail," she yelled, tossing down the vine. When I say 'tug,' swim away as fast as you can."

Whale tied the vine to her tail, muttering that this was the dumbest thing she had ever done.

"Now I will go and tie the other end around my waist," said Rabbit, and she went into the forest.

Rabbit concealed herself in the bushes. Then she yelled in her loudest voice, "Tug!"

Elephant slowly strolled away, still munching on the branch she had bitten off. Suddenly, she felt a tug.

"Wow, Rabbit is stronger than I expected," she said.

The tug became stronger and Elephant tugged hard, then harder and harder. She found herself at a standstill.

Meanwhile, Whale swam slowly out to sea. She was in for a shock, too. The vine tightened around her tail and would not budge.

"This is ridiculous. Rabbit could not be this strong," she exclaimed.

But, no matter how much she wiggled and tugged, she was stuck.

Before long the vine began to separate. Then it snapped.

Whale fell back in the water with a huge splash, and Elephant landed on her rear with a bump.

Rabbit crept out of the bushes and smiled.

"That was excellent," she declared.

After this, Elephant and Whale treated Rabbit with respect.

→ Circle the correct answer.

1. Rabbit took the vine first to

   (a) Elephant.   (b) Whale.

2. Elephant tied the vine around her

   (a) trunk.   (b) waist.

3. Whale tied the vine around her

   (a) waist.   (b) tail.

4. Rabbit hid in

   (a) the bushes.   (b) a tree.

5. Rabbit won the tug-of-war by

   (a) strength.   (b) a clever trick.

✎ Write your own animal story. You can write about real animals you know, such as your pet dog, or you can make up an imaginary story about animals.

_____

_____

_____

_____

_____

_____

_____

_____

_____

_____

_____

_____

_____

_____

Part Two: Unexpected Sounds

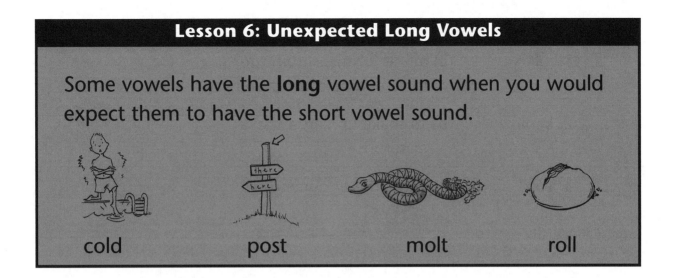

Lesson 6: Unexpected Long Vowels

Some vowels have the **long** vowel sound when you would expect them to have the short vowel sound.

cold   post   molt   roll

Sound out the letters to read each word.

old	bold	fold	gold
	hold	sold	told
ost	host	post	most
olt	bolt	jolt	volt
oll	poll	toll	troll
	knoll	scroll	stroll

→ Read the word in the box. Then circle the words in the same row that have the same long vowel sound.

host	hot	sold	boat	box	hope
poll	pole	shout	toad	pot	gold
old	top	post	soon	soap	cot
bolt	road	hole	rode	foot	job

→ Match the words with their meanings.

____ 1. jolt   (a) a unit for measuring the force of an electric current

____ 2. knoll   (b) to shake up, jar; a shock or surprise

____ 3. volt   (c) a mound; a rounded hill

____ 1. bolt   (a) an imaginary creature that lives in a cave or underground

____ 2. troll   (b) a person who has guests

____ 3. host   (c) a metal bar to lock a door; to run away suddenly

____ 1. scroll   (a) to walk in a slow, easy way; a slow, easy walk

____ 2. toll   (b) a roll of parchment paper, usually with writing on it

____ 3. stroll   (c) a fee or charge for the use of a bridge or road

The Troll

→ Choose a word from the list below to complete each sentence. Then write the word on the line.

toll   scroll   jolt   bolt   knoll   troll   host   stroll

1. The _____ spent most of the time in his cave.

2. But today he had been invited to a party _____ed by his old pal, gnome.

3. Troll was very excited because the letter inviting him to the party was in the form of a _____.

4. He left well before the expected time so he could slowly _____ there, taking his time.

5. But what a surprise he got when he came over the _____.

6. There was an ugly giant blocking the way and demanding a _____ from everyone passing along the road.

7. Seeing the mean giant gave Troll such a _____ that he turned around and _____ed back to his cave.

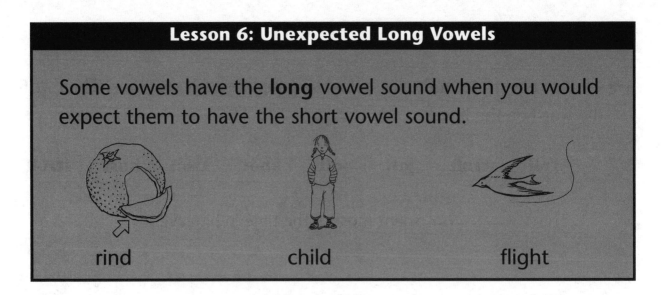

Lesson 6: Unexpected Long Vowels

Some vowels have the **long** vowel sound when you would expect them to have the short vowel sound.

rind   child   flight

➜ Sound out the letters to read each word.

ind	bind	find	hind	kind
	mind	wind	blind	grind
ild	child	mild	wild	
igh	high	sigh	thigh	right
	sight	fight	light	tight
	fright	bright	might	flight

➜ Draw a line between the words that have the **long i** sound.

light	bird	find	fit	wild	skirt
lid	white	first	fine	win	tight
mind	pie	crisp	stir	rip	mild
limb	lip	ice	sight	right	mitt

→ Match the beginning with the end of the words. Write the word on the line.

___ 1. moon   (a) night   _____

___ 2. slight   (b) light   _____

___ 3. mid   (c) ly   _____

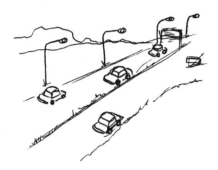

___ 1. fright   (a) way _____

___ 2. high   (b) y   _____

___ 3. wind   (c) en   _____

___ 1. be   (a) er   _____

___ 2. sigh   (b) hind   _____

___ 3. grind   (c) ing   _____

Trip to the Airport

➜ Choose a word from the list below to complete each sentence. Then write the word on the line.

delighted   flight   night   moonlight   highway   frightening

1. The lamps shone brightly, lighting up the _____ sky.

2. But as Maria and Tom left the main road, it was _____ that lighted the way.

3. Passing through the dark forest was _____ .

4. They knew they had to take the _____ to get to the airport, so they quickly drove on.

5. They were meeting the basketball team, whose _____ was due in at midnight.

6. They were _____ when they got to the airport in good time.

7. They wanted to be there to welcome their team because it had won the championship.

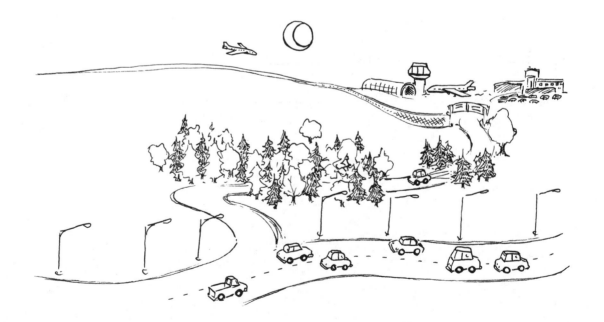

The First Flight

It is hard to think of the days when there were no airplanes. How long ago do you think the first flight took place?

(a) 50 years ago   (b) 100 years ago   (c) 200 years ago

 Now read the story of the Wright brothers' first flight.

Bishop Wright had been away, so he decided to bring his boys, Wilbur aged 11 and Orville aged 7, a present. It was a bat. No, it was not a baseball bat. Nor was it one of those creatures that flies at night and hangs upside down to sleep. It was a flying toy powered by a rubber band.

The Wright brothers enjoyed playing with this strange toy that flew through the air. They had always been interested in building things, so now they began trying to make toys that flew. Their models got bigger and better. Meanwhile, the boys learned about flight.

Wilbur and Orville got along well and went into business together. First they started a printing company, designing their own presses. Then they made and repaired bicycles.

Sending something into the air, however, continued to be their main interest. They started to build machines that might be able to go into the air. At last they decided to try out one such machine, a glider. They found a good site for their test in Kitty Hawk, North Carolina. The site had sand (for soft landings), wind (to keep the machine up), and privacy (so that people would not see or find out what they were doing).

The Wright brothers tried out their glider for more than two years. At first they camped out in a tent on the beach. But they discovered that it was hard to live in a tent. The sand got into everything. The wind whipped things away. And the mosquitoes caused constant itching. Eventually, they moved into a shed that they shared with their glider.

The brothers kept working to improve their machine until, finally, on December 17, 1903, Orville got the glider off the ground. It was up for only 12 seconds, but it was the first time a machine, under the control of a pilot, was in flight.

That day they made several flights. The longest lasted 59 seconds and went 852 feet. After this, the world was never the same. And it all started with a rubber-band-powered toy called "a bat."

→ Circle the correct answer.

1. How long ago was the first flight?

    (a) 50 years ago

    (b) 100 years ago

    (c) 200 years ago

2. What is the "bat" in the story?

    (a) a baseball bat

    (b) an animal

    (c) a rubber-band-powered flying toy

3. Which one of these did the Wright brothers NOT build?

    (a) printing presses

    (b) automobiles

    (c) bicycles

4. The Wright brothers chose Kitty Hawk to try out their machine because

    (a) it was windy.

    (b) there was no wind.

    (c) it was sunny.

5. When they found living in a tent too hard, the Wright brothers lived

    (a) in a house.

    (b) on a boat.

    (c) in a shed.

6. The first flight lasted for

    (a) 2 seconds

    (b) 12 seconds

    (c) 22 seconds

7. The longest flight lasted for

    (a) 59 seconds.

    (b) 59 minutes.

    (c) 59 hours.

8. What time of year was it?

    (a) September

    (b) December

    (c) April

The First North Americans

Who do you think were the first people to reach the North American *continent*? Circle the answer you think is correct.

(a) African Americans   (b) Asians (A'-zhens)   (c) Europeans (Yur-ə-pē'-əns)

How do you think the first people got here? Circle the answer you think is correct.

(a) They walked.   (b) They took a boat.   (c) They flew.

 In the old, old days, thousands of years ago, no one lived in what we now call North America. There were only wild plants, trees, and many kinds of animals.

It was not until about 30,000 years ago that the first people arrived. Scientists think that the first people came from Asia (A'-zha), and that they got here by walking.

Now if you look at the map of present-day Asia and North America you will see that it is impossible to walk from the continent of Asia to the continent of America. Why? Yes, the gap between the continents is covered with water.

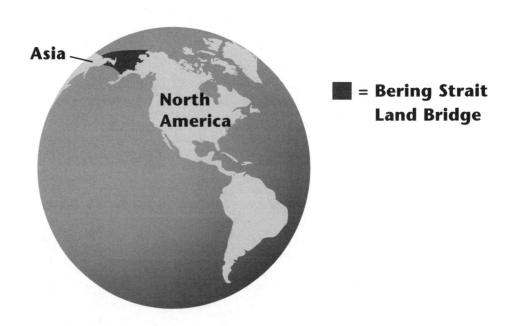

Asia

North America

■ = **Bering Strait Land Bridge**

So how did these people do it? The answer is that there was no water there at the time. The world was in the last ice age when the climate was very cold. Much of the water was frozen and the levels of the seas fell. Areas of land that once were under water became uncovered and dry.

Scientists say that part of the sea floor under the Bering Strait (the name of the waterway between the two continents) became dry ground. There was a bridge of land more than 1,000 miles wide, which made it possible to walk across this **strait** into North America.

Scientists think that the first people to reach the North American **continent** were not bold, frightened, or seeking a new life. They were not mighty fighters hoping to conquer the land. Nor were they looking for gold, jewels, or other **resources**. They were hunters who were following the animals who provided them with food, clothing, and shelter. They were nomads—people who do not live in one place but move about searching for food.

➜ Checking up: See if you are following the story.

Circle the correct answer.

1. The first people to reach the North American continent came from

    (a) Africa.

    (b) Asia.

    (c) Europe.

2. How many years ago did the first North Americans come here?

    (a) 30,000 years ago

    (b) 3,000 years ago

    (c) 300 years ago

3. What is between Asia and North America today?

    (a) land

    (b) forests

    (c) water

4. What was between Asia and North America when the first people came?

    (a) land

    (b) forests

    (c) water

5. When the first people came to North America, the climate was

    (a) hot.

    (b) cold.

    (c) mild.

6. What had happened to the seas at this time?

    (a) They had become higher.

    (b) They had become lower.

    (c) They had stayed at the same level.

7. How did the first people get to North America?

    (a) They walked.

    (b) They took a boat.

    (c) They flew.

8. Why did the first people come to the North American continent?

    (a) They wanted a new life.

    (b) They were fighters who wanted to conquer the land.

    (c) They were hunters who were following the animals they depended upon for food.

9. Nomads are

    (a) people who move from place to place.

    (b) people who stay in one place.

    (c) people who eat only plants.

The nomads traveled lightly because they were always moving from place to place. At night they unfolded dried animal skins to cover themselves and unpacked skin bags that held their stone tools. They made a fire for cooking and warmth. The fire also kept away the many wild animals.

Some of the animals were huge. There were giant bison that were like very large buffalo. There were also enormous elephants called mammoths. Mammoths stood nearly as high as a two-story house, with thighs as wide as tree trunks, long curling tusks, and thick, woolly hair.

These huge animals gradually disappeared and became **extinct**. Scientists think this was because the climate became **milder** (meaning warmer), and they were unable to **adapt** to the temperature change. With their long, thick woolly hair, mammoths would definitely have found the climate most uncomfortable. And mammoths were not able to **molt** (shed their covering) like snakes do.

The first North Americans continued to cross the land bridge from Asia for about 20,000 years. Then, as the milder climate melted the ice and caused the seas to rise again, water covered the land. It was no longer possible to reach the North American continent.

Meanwhile, the first people who came to North America and those that followed began to spread out and settle in new areas. They changed their nomadic way of life and began to raise animals and grow crops in the northwest, southwest, central, and eastern regions of the continent. In these places they learned to adapt to new conditions. They developed new kinds of foods, clothing, and shelter that took advantage of the **resources** available to them. In time, the people in each area developed their own way of life, or **culture**.

These first people to reach North American deserve our respect and admiration for establishing thriving communities from the wilderness. They are, of course, the ancestors of Native Americans.

→ Circle the correct answer.

1. The nomads "traveled lightly" means

    (a) they traveled only when it was light.

    (b) they always carried lights with them.

    (c) they did not carry much.

2. The nomads did NOT burn fires to

    (a) keep warm.

    (b) burn the shrubs so they could grow food.

    (c) cook meat.

3. The mammoths were like very large

    (a) buffalo.

    (b) elephants.

    (c) monkeys.

4. The mammoths were

    (a) as big as a car.

    (b) as wide as a tree trunk.

    (c) as high as a two-story house.

5. The huge animals died out because

    (a) it became too hot.

    (b) it became too cold.

    (c) they killed each other off.

6. People stopped coming to North America because

    (a) a wide crack developed in the land.

    (b) forests grew up, making it difficult to pass through.

    (c) water covered the land.

7. When the first Americans settled in different regions of the continent, they

    (a) continued to live the same way.

    (b) changed their way of life in the same way.

    (c) they changed their way of life depending on where they settled.

8. The first Americans are the ancestors of

    (a) African Americans

    (b) Latin Americans

    (c) Native Americans

➜ Match the words with their meanings.

____ 1. extinct   (a) a narrow body of water joining two larger ones

____ 2. strait   (b) to die out

____ 3. resources   (c) a supply of something useful

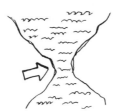

____ 1. continent   (a) gentle; not harsh

____ 2. molt   (b) a large land area surrounded by water

____ 3. mild   (c) to shed a coat or outer covering of skin or feathers

____ 1. culture   (a) becoming strong, successful

____ 2. adapt   (b) a way of life

____ 3. thriving   (c) to change to make fit or make usable

➜ Write the correct words on the line to complete the sentences.

mild   Strait   continent   molt

1. The Bering _____ is a body of water that separates Asia from North America.

2. Snakes renew their skins by _____ing.

3. Asia, Australia, and America are all _____s.

4. The winter was surprisingly _____ , with warm temperatures.

extinct   adapt   culture   thriving

5. The dinosaurs became _____ thousands of years ago.

6. Maria told us about the history and _____ of her country, Brazil.

7. The stores in the mall were _____ because many people shopped there.

8. The first Native Americans _____ed to their new environments.

✎ The passage on pages 79–80 says that after the Wright brothers' success in flying their machine, "the world was never the same." Write about the ways that flying has changed the world and people's lives.

_____

_____

_____

_____

_____

_____

_____

_____

_____

_____

_____

_____

_____

_____

_____

Lesson 7: Unexpected Vowel Sounds

Some vowels have **unexpected** sounds.

one month couple bull

Sound out the letters to read each word.

short u:	won	done	son	ton
	love	dove	above	brother
	glove	shove	month	mother

touch young trouble double country

gh with f sound: rough tough enough

flood blood

These words do not have the short u sound. They have the oo sound as in *foot.*

put pull full push bull

→ Draw a line between the words that have the same vowel sound.

push	bud	trouble	cuddle	month	wool
flood	book	bull	look	full	hunt
young	fun	cookie	country	pull	good
push	wood	put	cup	glove	shut

→ Find a word from the list that is the opposite of each word. A word that is the opposite is called an **antonym.** Write the antonym on the line.

rough   won   done   young

brother   love   full   above   pull

1. push _____

2. empty _____

3. old _____

4. sister _____

5. smooth _____

6. hate _____

7. below _____

8. unfinished _____

9. lost _____

The Young Family

Read slowly and carefully so you do not miss the details. See if you can answer the questions without looking back at the story. It will be a challenge.

John and Mary Young have a large house in the country. It's good that it is large, because many people in their family live with them. First there are their twin sons, Jake and Justin, whom Mary jokingly calls her "double trouble." They still live at home even though they now work.

John's brother Eli lives with the Youngs. He has the room above the garage. Mary's mother, Jo Ann, moved in a month ago. Her bedroom is on the first floor because she has trouble climbing stairs.

When Jake got married, his wife Lisa moved into the house with him. A few years later they had a son called Jock and a girl called Jasmine. The house is really full now with all of Jock's and Jasmine's toys and games.

Then, every so often, Mary's sister Pearl and her daughter Andrea love to come and stay with the Youngs.

Despite the house being so crowded, the Youngs enjoy being together.

➔ Write the correct answer on the line.

1. What are the names of Mary Young's "double trouble"?

_____   _____

2. What is the name of John Young's brother?

_____

3. What is the name of Jake's wife?

_____

4. Jock is

    (a) the son of _____ and _____ .

    (b) the grandson of _____ and _____ .

    (c) the nephew of _____ .

5. What is the name of Mary's sister? _____

That was hard. Reread the story to see if you answered the questions correctly. Then see if you can complete the Young family tree.

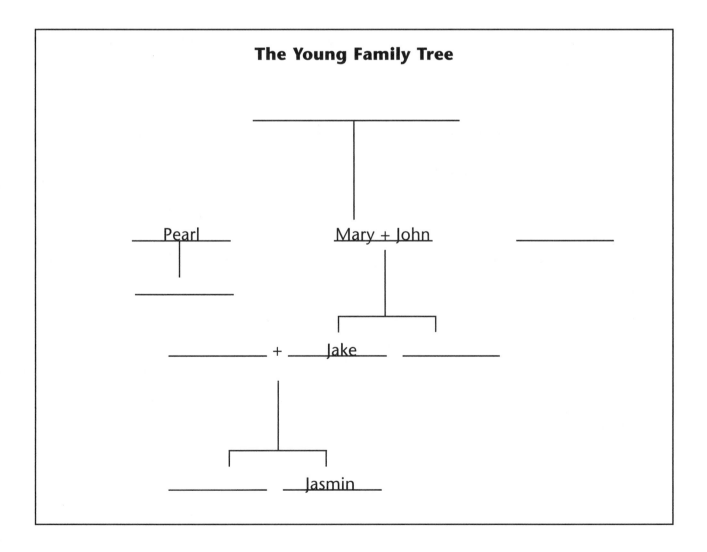

The Young Family Tree

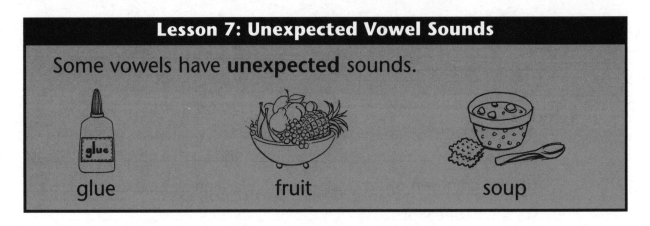

Lesson 7: Unexpected Vowel Sounds

Some vowels have **unexpected** sounds.

glue   fruit   soup

Sound out the letters to read each word.

These words have the sound of oo as in *moon*.

ue	blue	true	hue	glue
ui	fruit	suit	juice	
	bruise	cruise	recruit	
ou	you	your	youth	
	group	soup	route	
	routine	wound	through	
o	lose	move	prove	

→ Say the name of the word in the box. Then circle the words in the row that have the same vowel sound.

true	boot	good	youth	town
soup	house	food	wool	roof
suit	pool	prove	look	lose

Juan and Kim's First Flight

→ Learn the meanings of these words.

1. hue: color

2. cruise: to move smoothly and not too fast; to sail or move about

3. recruit: to hire or get; a new member of a group

4. route: a road; a way to travel

5. routine: a regular way of doing something

6. prove: to show something is true or correct

| **Why were Juan and Kim so excited?** |

Read about Juan and Kim's adventure. Choose one of the words on this page to complete each sentence. Write the word on the line.

This was not a _____ day in the lives of Juan and Kim. They had never flown before. But here they were taking a _____ three miles above the ground.

This all started two months ago when their teacher _____ed them to try out for the school spelling bee, which they won. Then they came first and second in the state contest. Now they were on _____ to Washington, D.C., for the finals.

It was evening as their jet flew over the city. The sky was orange with a reddish _____ as the sun was setting.

"This is awesome," said Juan as he looked down on the row of buildings and monuments.

"This _____s that all the hard work we put into the contest has paid off. Even if we don't win, we will have had this great trip," replied Kim.

Camping Trip

Have you been on a camping trip? What do you think a camping trip would be like?

 As you read the passage, look out for the words you learned on page 94.

Maria saw a notice for a camping trip on the school bulletin board. She had never been camping. She read the notice and decided it would be fun. This is what the notice said.

SIGN UP FOR THE FALL CAMPING TRIP

Join your classmates for a true camping experience—two days and nights in the Blue Ridge Mountains.

No equipment needed. What to wear? Bring comfortable shoes for walking and hiking and a swimming suit (we'll swim if the water's not too cold). The group will be small, so sign up soon.

We will teach you to

- follow a route on the map so if you lose your way you won't get lost.

- eat a healthy diet with plenty of fruits and juices while you're on the move.

- heat soup and hot dogs over a campfire.

- learn first aid so you can treat cuts, bruises, and wounds in case you ever get hurt.

We will prove to you that camping is a great way to spend a few days.

→ Reread the passage. Circle the words you learned on page 94 even if they are repeated.

How many did you find: _____ . If you did not find 22, go back over the passage.

Lesson 7: Unexpected Vowel Sounds

Some vowels have **unexpected** sounds.

ball   chalk   salt   wasp

Sound out the letters to read each word.

all	call	fall	hall
	tall	wall	small
alk	talk	walk	stalk
alt	halt	malt	salt

When **a** follows **w**, it has a different sound.

was	want	water
swap	what	swamp
wand	wander	swallow
swat	watch	walnut

→ Draw a line between the two words in each box that have the same vowel sound.

wall	can	want	way	ate	malt
cape	small	what	wait	salt	hand
stalk	camp	ant	play	was	hat
walk	rain	fall	wall	has	water

→ Words that have the same, or a similar, meaning are called **synonyms.** Find a synonym for each of these words from the list below. Write the synonym on the line.

wander   fall   swap   walk   tall   watch   small   halt   talk

1. autumn _____

2. stroll _____

3. trade _____

4. tiny _____

5. stop _____

6. high _____

7. look _____

8. roam _____

9. speak _____

→ Draw a line to the correct ending of each sentence.

1. Swallows fly south   in a swamp.

2. Frogs often live   in water.

3. Mosquitoes thrive where there   in the fall.

4. Corn grows   in a shell

5. A watch is worn   on a wrist.

6. A walnut grows   on a stalk.

7. Raindrops form in clouds when tiny water droplets   cold things like leaves or a car window.

8. Rivers start as   join together.

9. Frost forms at night when damp air touches   small streams.

What Is a Rainbow?

How many colors are there in a rainbow?

(a) 3   (b) 5   (c) 7

 Read the passage to learn what a rainbow is and why it appears in the sky.

What is a rainbow? It is an arc of colors that appear in the sky when sunlight shines through drops of water when it rains. The light breaks up into seven colors, which appear in this order (from the outside of the arc to the inside): red, orange, yellow, green, blue, indigo (deep violet-blue), and violet.

Why are there different colors? There are different colors because the white light of the sun is made up of many colors that only look white when they are combined. We see different colors because each color is bent by a different amount in passing through air or water. Red light is bent the most so it appears on the outside of the rainbow.

Rainbows usually last for only a few minutes. The next time the sun comes out during a rain shower, look for it or you may miss it.

Also, be sure to have your back to the sun.

This is how the light reaches your eyes.

You do not always have to be out in the rain to see a rainbow. You can make your own rainbow at home or in the classroom.

Fill a glass with water. Place a flat sheet of white paper in front of a sunny window. Put the glass of water on the paper and you will see bands of colored lights on the paper.

→ Circle the correct answer.

1. How many colors are there in a rainbow?

    (a) 3

    (b) 5

    (c) 7

2. Which color appears on the inside of the rainbow?

    (a) red

    (b) violet

3. Which color comes between yellow and blue?

    (a) green

    (b) indigo

4. What color is indigo?

    (a) a reddish color

    (b) deep violet-blue

5. Which color is bent the most?

    (a) red

    (b) blue

6. Light bends by different amounts when it

    (a) rains a lot.

    (b) travels through air or water.

7. What color does the light of the sun appear as?

    (a) white

    (b) orange

8. To see a rainbow you must

    (a) have your back to the sun.

    (b) face the sun.

9. You can make your own rainbow by using

    (a) glass of water.

    (b) a glass of orange juice.

The Story of the First Rainbow

Who made all the colors of the rainbow live in peace?

(a) the sun   (b) the rain

You have found out why a rainbow appears in nature. Here is a folk tale about how the first rainbow was created.

Green started the quarrel between the colors. It was at their yearly party when they got together to talk and catch up on each other's news. The quarrel was about who was best.

"I am the most important," said **Green.** "Nature would not be possible without me. I give color to the trees, plants, and grasses that supply all the animals with food. I am needed for life," Green bragged.

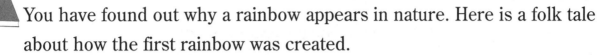

"Hey, wait a minute," **Blue** cried. "What about the blue sea and sky? Aren't they more important? They certainly are bigger than anything that is green. Green is just on the surface, but blue goes deep and distant. And another thing, if you look from space, everything is blue. That is why we are called the blue planet."

"I wouldn't swap my place for anything," exclaimed **Yellow.** "I shine through the sun, moon, and stars that give light to day and night. There would be no life without the warmth of the sun's yellow rays. And what would the nights be like without the changing moon and those jewels of the sky that sparkle in the darkness?

"Excuse me," interrupted **Orange.** "I may not be as common as you three, but I stand out. I am warm and glowing. I start each day with the most glorious sunrise and end it with the most beautiful sunset. I also want to point out that I am the color of fall, the last touch of life before winter comes. I paint the loveliest flower. I am found in the healthiest foods, such as oranges, carrots, and pumpkins. I would be sorely missed if I disappeared."

→ Checking up: See if you are following the story. Each color gave a reason why it was the best color. Match the color with the reason.

_____ 1. green   (a) is found in healthy foods

_____ 2. blue   (b) gives color to nature

_____ 3. yellow   (c) goes deep and distant

_____ 4. orange   (d) provides the jewels of the sky

"I wish you all would stop bragging," said **Red,** getting angrier by the minute. "It's obvious that I am the best and most powerful color. Look how bright I am. I am danger and courage. I am fire and blood. I am full of life. I am life itself."

"You are not full of life—you are too full of yourself! And that goes for all of you," **Purple** called out. Purple stood up, tall, straight, and proud, and went on. "I, on the other hand, have respect and power. I am the color of royalty and rules. I stand for wisdom, dignity, and honesty. People listen to me and do what I say."

The only person who had not spoken was **Indigo.** But Indigo was not going to be left out. Although shy, Indigo was determined to speak. As soon as Purple stopped talking, Indigo took a deep breath, swallowed hard, and blurted out. "I know I am quiet and you hardly notice me, but I am extremely valuable. I am not loud and talkative like you, but I represent peace and quiet. I am the friend of silence. I provide the contrast to you noisy, pushy colors. I am the twilight that calms. I am necessary for friendship and harmony, which we cannot survive without."

→ Checking up: See if you are following the story. Match the color with the reason each color gave for being the best.

_____ 1. red   (a) stands for wisdom, dignity, and honesty

_____ 2. purple   (b) represents peace and quiet

_____ 3. indigo   (c) is fire and blood

 Nobody really listened to Indigo. The colors were too busy boasting and arguing. Their voices became louder and louder. Suddenly, there was a flash and a crash. It was lightning and thunder. Rain poured down, soaking the colors that were huddled together against the wet and cold.

They were startled to hear Rain's deep voice over the storm.

"I've had enough of your bragging and quarreling. What's wrong with you? Can't you see that you each have a purpose? You don't have to prove that you are the best because you are all the best at what you do. Now, come and join hands and follow me."

The colors held hands and looked up at Rain as she said, "Now I want you all to live in peace. To help you do this, whenever it rains, you will unite and stretch in a great arc across the sky. It will be a beautiful sight and will show that we can live together even though we don't always agree."

And so that is why you can see a rainbow stretched across the sky after a rainfall.

→ Circle the correct answer.

1. Who started the quarrel between the colors?

    (a) red

    (b) green

2. The colors stopped arguing

    (a) when got tired of arguing.

    (b) when there was a thunderstorm.

3. Who told the colors to stop arguing?

    (a) the rain

    (b) the sun

4. How could each color be the best?

    (a) It was not possible.

    (b) Each color was best at what it did.

5. What were the colors told to do when it rained?

    (a) hold hands and stretch across the sky in an arc

    (b) group together to form one color

▲ **Challenge: Can you remember the order of colors in a rainbow? If you cannot, go back over the passage on page 100. Write the order on the lines.**

1. _____   5. _____

2. _____   6. _____

3. _____   7. _____

4. _____

✎ The notice on the bulletin board on page 96 tells about a camping trip. Write about why you would like to go on a camping trip, or why not.

_____

_____

_____

_____

_____

_____

_____

_____

_____

_____

_____

_____

_____

_____

_____

_____

_____

Lesson 8: Ei and Ey

When two vowels come together, they can have either the **regular** sound or an **unexpected** sound.

ceiling

reindeer

Sound out the letters to read each word.

ei: regular **sound of** long e

either	seize	leisure
ceiling	neither	receive
deceive	weird	conceited

ei/ey: unexpected **sound of** long a

eight	veins	weigh	they
sleigh	grey	obey	reins
prey	reign	neighbor	convey

→ Draw a line between the words that have the same long vowel sound.

sleigh	street	receive	weigh	they	say
deceive	way	need	late	seize	please
prey	weird	eight	seat	veil	whale
peek	pray	neither	gain	leisure	leaf

→ Write the correct homophone on the line. Remember: Homophones are words that sound the same but have different spellings and meanings.

ate   eight

1. Flora _____ breakfast quickly.

2. Then at _____ o'clock she ran to catch the bus.

way   weigh

3. Flora was nearly late because the books she had to carry _____ed a ton.

4. It was a long _____ to the bus stop.

reign   rain

5. Just as Flora got on the bus, it began to _____ .

6. As soon as she was on the bus Flora got out her history book because she had a test on the _____ of Queen Elizabeth.

vein   vain

7. In _____ Flora tried to remember all the dates.

8. Next, she took out her science book and studied the picture of a leaf showing its tiny _____s and jagged edges.

→ Fill in the blanks by selecting the word that fits best. Cross out each word when you use it.

weird   deceive   seize   conceited

1. **When** you grab hold of something, you _____ it.

2. **When** you make someone believe something that is not true, you _____ that person.

3. **When** you think that something is strange, you might call it _____.

4. **When** people are full of themselves, they are _____.

convey   veins   prey   reins

5. **When** the blood travels back to the heart, it goes along _____.

6. **When** an animal hunts another animal for food, it _____ s on the animal.

7. **When** riders want to control a horse, they use _____.

8. **When** you want to make something known by communicating it, you _____ it.

Trip to the Moon

 Read the story and write in the missing words. Then reread the story to see if it makes sense.

chief   convey   vein   They

Three astronauts—Neil Armstrong, Buzz Aldrin, and Michael Collins—were going to be the first to find out what a trip to the moon would be like. They sat together in the small spacecraft, Apollo 11, and waited. _____ were about to go on one of the most exciting voyages in history. It was July 16, 1969, and they were off to the moon.

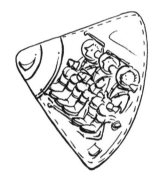

Over the intercom, the _____ scientist_____ed everyone's best wishes.

Suddenly, there was an incredibly loud, booming sound. Apollo 11 jerked and shook. The astronauts were pushed back in their seats. Their hearts pounded, pushing blood into every _____.

received   neighboring   obey   neither   weightless   weird

The astronauts never looked away from the controls, ready to _____ any command they _____ in case anything went wrong.

The first rocket dropped off, then the second, and then the third. The astronauts looked out their windows. They saw one vast planet of land and sea. There were no separate or _____ countries.

The astronauts were now _____ in space. It was a _____ feeling, but they had been training for this for a long time. They were _____ afraid nor excited.

grey   leisure   eight

There was little _____ time on the trip, but they did get to sleep at night. By the third day, July 19, they fired a rocket to go into orbit around the moon. On July 20, they were ready to land on the moon.

Now they had a good view of the _____ mountains and craters and the rough surface of the moon.

The spacecraft divided into two sections. Armstrong and Aldrin headed for the moon in the landing craft, *Eagle.* Collins stayed behind in the command module, *Columbia.*

Armstrong and Aldrin successfully landed on the moon.

"The *Eagle* has landed," Armstrong announced proudly.

Almost a quarter of a million miles away, people everywhere cheered.

_____ days later, the astronauts were home again.

When two vowels come together they can have either the **regular** sound or an **unexpected** sound.

pie

thief

Sound out the letters to read each word.

ie: regular **sound of** long i

lie	die	tie	cried
dried	tried	fried	replied

ie: unexpected **sound of** long e

brief	chief	fierce	piece
grieve	field	yield	niece
shield	shriek	cookie	relief
puppies	believe	pierce	achieve

Learn to read these words: friend   review

→ Draw a line between the words that have the same **long** vowel sound.

shield	dried	cried	niece	brief	lie
pierce	replied	field	tie	fried	yield
hide	peace	cookie	sky	shriek	tried
piece	die	pie	monkey	stripe	bean

Ant and Bird

Ant says she believes that *one good turn deserves another*. What does this saying mean?

 Read the story to find out.

Ant and her friends found some cookies that were left from a picnic in a nearby field. They were scurrying back and forth to their homes with as many crumbs as they could carry.

It was very tiring, and Ant became thirsty.

"I'll take a brief rest and go down to the river for a drink," she said to herself.

Just as she reached the river, a wave came up and carried her away.

"Help! Help!" Ant shrieked.

Frantically, Ant tried to stay afloat.

For a brief moment she thought she was going to die. But she was lucky. Bird had seen what had happened.

She flew down from the tree where she had been perching.

"Hold on!" she cried.

Quickly Bird plucked a leaf from a branch. Then she flew over Ant and dropped the leaf beside her. Ant heaved herself on to the leaf and paddled to shore.

"Thank you, thank you," exclaimed Ant, relieved to be out of the water.

"No problem," replied Bird.

Bird dried off Ant with a piece of a flower petal and said, "Now lie down here on this grassy patch and rest."

Ant dozed off. Then a noise woke her. She saw Cat looking up at the tree where Bird was also dozing.

"Oh, no, you don't!" cried Ant fiercely, guessing what was on Cat's mind.

Ant nipped Cat on her paw.

"Ouch!" cried Cat.

Cat's cry woke up Bird, and she flew to safety.

Ant breathed a sigh of relief. She was glad she had helped her new friend because she had always believed that **one good turn deserves another.**

➜ What is the meaning of the saying "One good turn deserves another"? Circle the correct answer.

(a) If someone helps you, you can expect that person to help you again.

(b) If someone helps you, you should help him or her in return.

Can You Believe It?

How much pancake batter do you get if you fill one bowl with wheat flour, a second bowl (of the same size) with water, and you mix the contents together?

(a) just over one full bowl

(b) just over two full bowls

(c) just over three full bowls

 Read the passage to see if you are correct.

Walter tried a recipe for pancakes. The chief ingredients were wheat flour and water. He took out two bowls of the same size. He filled one with wheat flour and one with water. He then took out a third, bigger bowl and gradually mixed the flour and water together. Walter believed that the batter would fill both of the original bowls.

But no, there was room for nearly all the batter in just one of the bowls.

"Why doesn't the batter fill both bowls?" Walter asked his mom.

"Well," his mom replied, "It's because the water squeezes into the spaces between the tiny granules, or pieces, of dry flour. And the granules are made of coiled molecules that absorb the water."

"What are coiled molecules?" asked Walter.

"Everything is made up of very small pieces called **molecules.** These pieces are so small you can't see them with your eyes. **Coiled** means 'wound up,' as in a coil of rope. The molecules in flour are wound in rings or spirals."

"Well, at least we have enough to make pancakes for both of us," laughed Walter. And he put some of the batter into the frying pan.

→ Did you get the correct answer?

1. When you mix the contents of a bowl full of wheat flour and a bowl of water you get

   (a) just over one full bowl.

   (b) just over two full bowls.

   (c) just over three full bowls.

2. Why do you not get two full bowls?

   (a) The water changes into a gas.

   (b) The water is absorbed by the flour.

3. *Molecules* are

   (a) very small pieces that something is made of.

   (b) very small pancakes.

4. What does "coiled" mean?

   (a) long and straight

   (b) winding around in rings or spirals

→ There are 5 **ie** words in the passage, including the title. Find the words and write them under the correct headings.

long i sound   **long e sound**

_____   _____

_____   _____

_____   _____

First Relatives: A Book Review of
The Girl Who Loved Wild Horses

The next passage is a book review, which is like a book report. A book review

- explains what happens (the plot) and highlights a few events from the story.
- describes briefly the main characters.
- describes where the story takes place (the setting).
- explains the theme or main idea.
- gives the reader's opinion of the book—if it is interesting or boring, funny or sad, too long or just right.

Who do you think are the "first relatives" of Native Americans?

 Read the review and see if you would like to read *The Girl Who Loved Wild Horses.**

I loved *The Girl Who Loved Wild Horses* by Paul Goble. It is the kind of story that keeps you turning the pages to see what happens next. The author is well known for his retellings of Native American legends. He also illustrates his books with colorful, lively drawings.

The Girl Who Loved Wild Horses is a Native American story about a girl who lives happily with her parents and tribe. They are always moving from place to place because they follow the buffalo they depend on for food and shelter. The girl has a great love for horses. She spends as much time as she can with them and seems to understand them.

One day, when she is with the horses, a fierce storm suddenly begins. It frightens the horses, and they gallop away. The girl shrieks to the horses to call them back, but it is no use. She quickly seizes the mane of a horse and jumps on its back. It is not until the storm stops that the horses stop running. By this time the girl realizes they are far from home and hopelessly lost.

*Published by Simon & Schuster (Alladin Paperbacks), New York, 1993.

A beautiful spotted stallion appears. He tells her that he is the chief of the wild horses. He invites her to join them. She does this happily for a year. Then hunters from her tribe discover her, but they are fiercely driven away by the stallion. Later, members of the tribe come and take the girl back.

The girl is happy to be home with her parents, but she misses her wild horse friends. The stallion comes every night to a nearby hilltop and neighs sadly, calling her back.

What happens to the girl? Does she go back to be with the stallion and the wild horses? You must read the story to find out.

➜ Checking up: See if you are following the review. Circle the correct answer.

1. Which culture does the story come from?

    (a) African American

    (b) Native American

2. The tribe moved from place to place to follow

    (a) the wild horses.

    (b) the buffalo.

3. The girl had a great love for

    (a) horses.

    (b) buffalo.

4. The horses galloped off because

    (a) the girl shrieked at them.

    (b) a storm came.

5. The girl stayed with the wild horses for

    (a) one month.

    (b) one year.

6. What happened to the girl?

    (a) She joins the wild horses again.

    (b) The review does not say what the girl does.

7. What you would like the girl to do?

    (a) stay with her parents and the tribe

    (b) join the stallion and the wild horses

 The two main characters in *The Girl Who Loved Wild Horses* are the girl, and, you guessed it, the stallion. Goble shows the wonderful relationship they have and how they both enjoy the freedom of the wild.

The friendship between the girl and the stallion is the theme of the book. The story shows the closeness between Native Americans and the wild horses that they call "first relatives." It also shows how Native Americans love nature and live in harmony with it.

The story takes place on the Great Plains, that vast expanse of land where millions of buffalo once roamed.*

I enjoyed *The Girl Who Loved Wild Horses*. It is a short book with vivid illustrations that make the story seem real. I am sure you will enjoy it too.

➔ Circle the correct answer.

1. The "first relatives" of Native Americans referred to in the review are

    (a) members of the tribe.

    (b) horses.

*See Lesson 9, pages 127–128 for more information about the Plains Indians.

2. The major event in the story that caused a change in the girl's life was

(a) a storm that caused the horses to gallop away.

(b) a buffalo stampede that forced the tribe to move.

3. The main characters in the story are

(a) the girl and her parents.

(b) the girl and the stallion.

4. The story takes place

(a) on the Great Plains.

(b) in the Blue Ridge Mountains.

5. The theme of the story is

(a) the closeness between Native Americans, horses, and nature.

(b) the closeness between two Native American tribes.

6. Did the person reviewing the book enjoy the book?

(a) yes

(b) no

Read a book that you think looks interesting. Then write a review of the story. Remember to include these key points:

- Explain what happens (the plot) and highlight a few events from the story.

- Describe briefly the main characters.

- Describe where the story takes place (the setting).

- Explain the theme or main idea.

- Give your opinion of the book—why you did or did not enjoy it.

Lesson 9: Syllables

When two or more consonants come between two vowels in a word, first try to divide the word between the first two consonants.

walnut

Divide compound words (two words put together) between the two words.

highway

Remember: When two vowels come together and they make one sound, there is only one syllable.

fruit   you   blood   seize

→ Circle the vowels. Write the number of vowels in each word. Then write the number of vowel sounds and syllables in each word.

	Vowels	Vowel Sounds and Syllables		Vowels	Vowel Sounds and Syllables
golden	_____	_____	salt	_____	_____
binder	_____	_____	field	_____	_____
water	_____	_____	lighthouse	_____	_____
moonlight	_____	_____	toll	_____	_____
bold	_____	_____	campfire	_____	_____
swallow	_____	_____	hallway	_____	_____
suitcase	_____	_____	tough	_____	_____
bruise	_____	_____	believe	_____	_____
airport	_____	_____	soup	_____	_____
sidewalk	_____	_____	movement	_____	_____
cookies	_____	_____	sight	_____	_____
obey	_____	_____	neighborhood	_____	_____

→ Draw a line between the beginning and the end of each word.

neigh	ies	re	tine
cook	en	stroll	low
most	bor	swal	er
fright	ly	rou	cruit

eight	nough	young	en
e	sect	re	est
achieve	y	light	house
in	ment	gold	view

good	er	moth	try
wat	night	coun	plied
move	lieve	re	ly
be	ment	kind	er

The First Cultures of North America

When Native Americans settled in various parts of the United States, they had to adapt to different environments. Each group developed its own ways of living in the regions where it settled. How did each group adapt?

Read the passages to find out.

Pacific
Northwest
Indians

Plains
Indians

Eastern
Woodland
Indians

Southwest
Indians

The Eastern Woodland Indians

How did the Eastern Woodland Indians make use of the forest?

 The groups that settled in the Eastern woodlands, from the Mississippi River eastward, included the Algonquins (Al-gän'-kwəns) and the Iroquois (Eer'-ə-kwoy). The forest provided everything they needed. There were animals they could hunt for food and skins to make clothes. There were many rivers and lakes that provided water and fish. The trees in the forest supplied them with building materials for their homes, as well as fruit and nuts to eat.

The Algonquins and the Iroquois built large villages and large, long houses in which eight to ten families lived. To protect themselves, they fenced the village with tall logs driven upright into the ground.

The Eastern Woodland Indians prepared fields for growing crops using a method called "slash and burn." They cut deep rings around the tree trunks, which caused the trees to die. Then they set the trees on fire and planted crops between the dead stumps. Their crops included corn, squash, beans, and pumpkins. All the villagers worked together to farm, and they shared equally in the harvest. However, the soil became overused after about ten years and was no longer good for growing. Then the Indians moved on and settled somewhere else.

→ On the map on page 124, find the region where the Eastern Woodland Indians settled. Circle it.

→ Checking up: See if you are following the details. Circle the correct answer.

1. The forest of the Eastern Woodland Indians provided

    (a) many dangers.

    (b) everything they needed.

2. These Indians built their homes from

    (a) the skins of the animals they hunted.

    (b) trees from the forest.

3. Their homes were

    (a) small and round.

    (b) large and long.

4. "Slash and burn" was the way they

    (a) cleared the forest to grow crops.

    (b) hunted animals for food.

5. Which crop did the Eastern Woodland Indians NOT grow?

    (a) beans

    (b) peas

6. The villagers had to move on because the soil was no longer good for growing

    (a) every 10 years.

    (b) every 30 years.

The Plains Indians

How do you think the Plains Indians survived in a hard, dry land with little rainfall?

 The Great Plains stretch from the Mississippi River west to the Rocky Mountains. Most of the land is hard and dry because there is little rainfall. It is covered with short grass that has tough roots, making it difficult to till (dig) the soil to grow crops. There are few trees and not many rivers and streams. The wind sweeps across the land. The winters are extremely cold. The summers are very hot, sometimes reaching 100°F (38°C). Why would anyone want to settle on the Great Plains? And how could they survive? The answer is buffalo. Great herds of buffalo wandered the grassy land. The Great Plains Indians survived because they became hunters.

The buffalo supplied the Plains Indians with everything they needed—meat for food, skins for clothing, and bones for tools. They made blankets, clothes, and shoes from the tough skins, or hides, of the buffalo. Nothing was wasted. Even the stomach was used to make containers to hold water and cook in. Other parts of the buffalo were used to make sturdy strings for their hunting bows.

Buffalo hides were used to make tepees that the Plains Indians lived in. The tepees were made from twelve willow tree branches that were placed upright in a circle and tied together at the top. The branches were then wrapped with buffalo hide. The Plains Indians invented this building form because they needed homes that could be easily moved when they followed the buffalo.

➜ On the map on page 124, find the region where the Plains Indians settled. Circle it.

➜ Checking up: See if you are following the details. Circle the correct answer.

1. The area that stretches from the Mississippi River west to the Rocky Mountains is called

    (a) the Windy Plains.

    (b) the Great Plains.

2. In this region, crops

    (a) can be grown because rivers and streams provide water.

    (b) cannot be grown because short grass with tough roots makes it difficult to till the ground.

3. The climate of this region produces

    (a) cold winters and cool summers.

    (b) cold winters and hot summers.

4. The stomach of the buffalo was used to make

    (a) containers for water and cooking.

    (b) balls for games.

5. Tepees were made from

    (a) the bones and hides of the buffalo.

    (b) tree branches and the hides of the buffalo.

6. Tepees were useful because

    (a) they could be moved easily.

    (b) they lasted a long time.

The Southwest Indians

How did the Southwest Indians make a living in a dry, desert environment?

 The Southwest Indians also lived in a very difficult climate and environment. Much of the land was desert with very little rainfall and very few plants. Over the centuries the Southwest Indians found ways of farming despite the heat and dryness of the climate. In fact, they became among the most successful of all Native American farmers. They grew corn, beans, and squash. They also grew cotton, which they wove into cloth to make clothes and blankets. How did they do this? They irrigated their land by digging ditches to bring water to their crops from nearby rivers, streams, and lakes.

Among the Eastern Woodland Indians, the men hunted and fished while the women farmed. However, among the Southwest Indians, the men did the farming. The men also made cloth from cotton, and the older men did the weaving. The women ground the corn and did the cooking. They also made baskets and beautiful pottery, which they still make today.

The Southwest Indians came to be called the Pueblos (Pweb'-lohs). The first Spaniards gave them this name, which means "town," because they lived in communities.

Like other North American Indians, the Pueblos used materials they found in their environment to build their houses. These materials were mainly stone and clay. They made a clay mixture called 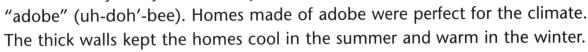 "adobe" (uh-doh'-bee). Homes made of adobe were perfect for the climate. The thick walls kept the homes cool in the summer and warm in the winter.

The homes were often attached to one another or built on top of one another. Some of them were like apartment buildings and rose four to five stories high.

Pueblo Indians include the Zunis (Zoo'-nees) and the Hopis (Hoh'-pees). These were peaceful people who believed in sharing work and cooperating. Later groups who came to the Southwest were the Apaches and the Navajos. These Indians were chiefly hunters and gatherers. They were also tough warriors who often raided the Pueblos's villages.

➜ On the map on page 124, find the region where the Southwest Indians settled. Circle it.

➜ Checking up: See if you are following the details. Circle the correct answer.

1. The environment of the Southwest Indians was

    (a) good.

    (b) difficult.

2. These Indians were able to farm in the dry climate because they

    (a) developed crops that needed little water.

    (b) brought water to the crops from rivers and lakes.

3. The women

    (a) farmed.

    (b) ground corn.

4. "Pueblo" is Spanish for

    (a) farmer.

    (b) town.

5. The adobe houses were made of

    (a) clay.

    (b) wood.

6. The Pueblos were

    (a) peaceful people.

    (b) tough warriors.

The Pacific Northwest Indians

Why did the Pacific Northwest Indians have more leisure time than the other Indian groups? How did they use their extra time?

 The Indians of the Pacific Northwest were fortunate. Their environment, from the coast of western North American into southeastern Canada, was ideal. The climate was mild. There was plenty of rain from the strong, wet winds that blew in from the Pacific Ocean. The soil was fertile, which meant that crops grew easily. Food was plentiful, and the giant trees provided the wood to build large, solid houses. There were also many rivers filled with salmon that swam up from the ocean to lay their eggs. There were even whales to hunt in the ocean. Yes, nature was good to these Indians.

Since living was easier for the Pacific Northwest Indians than for some other groups, they had enough leisure time to enjoy other activities. They became expert woodcrafters. They made wood furniture, pots, and bowls for their homes. They carved beautiful masks of wood and invented the totem pole.

Totem poles were carved from the trunks of trees. They were covered with beautiful carvings that either told a story or recorded an event. They usually carved an animal at the top because animals were important to them.

The Pacific Northwest Indians were also skillful at metalwork, and they made pottery and beautiful woven baskets.

→ On the map on page 124, find the region where the Pacific Northwest Indians settled. Circle it.

→ Checking up: See if you are following the details.

1. The climate in the Pacific Northwest was

    (a) mild.

    (b) harsh.

2. The Pacific Northwest Indians were able to build large houses because

    (a) they worked in large groups.

    (b) large trees grew in the region.

3. The passage suggests that Pacific Northwest Indians were more likely to eat

    (a) fish.

    (b) corn.

4. Pacific Northwest Indians had more leisure time than the other Indian groups because

    (a) they were better organized.

    (b) living was easier.

5. These Indians became

    (a) expert woodcrafters.

    (b) skillful farmers.

6. Totem poles carved from tree trunks were used

    (a) to frighten people away.

    (b) to tell a story or record an event.

➔ Match the beginning and the end of each sentence.

____ The Eastern Woodland Indians depended on	a) raise crops in a dry region.
____ The Plains Indians depended on	(b) forests.
____ The Southwest Indians developed a way to	(c) had time for leisure activities.
____ The Pacific Northwest Indians	(d) buffalo.

The First Being: A Chinese Myth

What are Yin and Yang? Why is an egg used as their symbol?

An old Chinese belief is that all things have an opposite. The day has night. The earth has sky. The opposites are called Yin and Yang. The symbol for Yin and Yang is an egg divided into the yolk and the white, the dark and the light parts. In this myth you will learn about Yin and Yang and why an egg is used as their symbol.

In the beginning there was no land, no sea, no sky, and no living creatures. There was only a small mass of space folded in upon itself in the shape of an egg. All the opposites were mixed together inside the egg. This caused complete disorder and chaos, mainly due to Yin and Yang.

Yin and Yang act in contrast to, or opposite, one another. They are darkness and light, night and day, cold and hot, wet and dry, down and up. Yin always stands for the dark side of things. Yang stands for the bright side of things.

There came a time when all the opposites led to disorder and chaos. This caused the egg to split. The heavier parts of the egg dropped to form the planet we now live on. The lighter parts floated up to form the sky. A hairy creature rolled out. He had two stubby horns pushing out from his forehead and two sharp tusks sticking out from his mouth. He was the first being, and his name was P'an-Ku.

For 18,000 years, P'an-Ku held apart the planet and the sky to keep the Yin and the Yang separate. A time came when P'an-Ku could no longer keep them apart. He was too tired. The weight had become too much.

As soon as P'an-Ku let go, there was the most thunderous sound. P'an-Ku's body twisted and twirled in the air and broke into pieces that scattered over the planet. P'an-Ku's head became mountains in the north, and his feet became mountains in the south. His arms became mountains in the west and east, and his stomach a mountain in the center.

P'an-Ku's eyes became the sun and the moon. His torso (the main part of the body) became the land. His hair became the trees and plants. His tears became the seas and rivers. His breath became the wind, while his voice became the sounds of the storm.

And not least of all, from P'an-Ku's body fell human beings. Where did they come from? They were formed from the fleas that sprang from his hair!

→ Circle the correct answer.

1. An old Chinese belief is that Yin and Yang stand for

    (a) the same.

    (b) the opposite.

2. An egg is used as a symbol for Yin and Yang because

    (a) they were enclosed in an egg.

    (b) they liked to eat eggs.

3. The egg split open because

    (a) P'an-Ku wanted to get out.

    (b) There was too much disorder and chaos inside the egg.

4. What did P'an-Ku do for 18,000 years?

    (a) He gradually became smaller.

    (b) He grew and kept the planet and sky, Yin and Yang, apart.

5. What happened to P'an-Ku when he could no longer keep the planet and sky apart?

    (a) He broke into pieces.

    (b) He curled up into an egg.

6. Draw a line between the pairs that match.

___ 1. P'an-Ku's hair became   (a) the sounds of the storm.

___ 2. P'an-Ku's eyes became   (b) mountains in the south.

___ 3. P'an-Ku's head became   (c) the seas and rivers.

___ 4. P'an-Ku's tears became   (d) the trees and plants.

___ 5. P'an-Ku's voice became   (e) mountains in the north.

___ 6. P'an-Ku's feet became   (f) the sun and the moon.

✎ Imagine you were one of the first Native Americans. Choose one of the groups you have read about and describe what it would be like to live in that environment. Talk about the climate, what you would eat and how you would get your food, and your home and the materials used to build it.

_____

_____

_____

_____

_____

_____

_____

_____

_____

_____

_____

_____

_____

_____

_____

Part Three: A Variety of Sounds

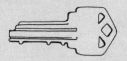

Lesson 10: Sounds of K

Lesson 11: Sounds of S

Lesson 12: Vowels with R

Lesson 13: Syllables

Lesson 10: Sounds of K

Several letters can make the **k** sound.

k: key   ck: sock   c: cat   ch: school   que: physique

Sound out the letters to read each word.

k	kid	keep	kind	kitchen
	like	turkey	milk	blanket
ck	lock	back	o'clock	luck
	sicken	necklace	stocking	check

c   **C** has the **k** sound when it comes before **a**, **o**, and **u**.

	cut	catch	cupboard	column
	call	comma	card	curl
ch	chorus	chromium	chord	chaos
	character	chemical	choir	chemistry
que	unique	antique	technique	physique

qu   **Qu** has the **kw** sound.

	quilt	quick	quantity	liquid
	equator			

➜ Draw a line between the pair of words that have the **k** sound.

cake ceiling	chocolate ice	unique cent
church antique	block choir	chemistry china
weaken piece	cotton pencil	city cycle
actor cheap	chop physique	chaos cloak

➜ Circle the missing letters that make the **k** sound. Then write the missing letters on the line.

1. Noah works out every day to develop his physi_____ .   ck   que

2. When Old Mother Hubbard went to the _____upboard,   k   c
   it was bare.

3. The director played a chord to start _____ orus practice.   ch   ck

4. In _____ emistry class, Chris learned about liquids.   k   ch

5. There were only five _____ aracters in the play.   que   ch

6. At ten o'_____ lock some of the class went to orchestra   c   k
   practice.

7. Carol's desk was in _____ aos after her new puppy chewed   que   ch
   on her papers.

8. You need excellent techni_____ to become a champion   que   ch
   swimmer.

→ Match the words with their meanings.

____1. unique   (a) an imaginary circle around the middle of the earth

____2. chaos   (b) one of a kind

____3. equator   (c) disorder

____1. chord   (a) a way of doing or making something

____2. technique (b) an amount; how much

____3. quantity   (c) a group of musical notes

____1. physique   (a) a person in a story or play

____2. character (b) a very hard metal

____3 chromium (c) the build and structure of the body

____1. chorus   (a) very old; an object that is very old

____2. chemistry (b) a group that sings together

____3. antique   (c) a study of the structure of matter

→ Write the words in the blanks where they fit best. Do the easiest words first and cross out words as you use them.

antique   chorus   equator   chemistry

chromium   chord   physique   chaos   unique

1. **If** you are asked to name the imaginary line around the middle of the globe, you would say it is the _____ .

2. **If** you blend several notes into a _____ , the sound is very pleasant.

3. **If** you eat well and work out, you will have a good _____ .

4. **If** you like to sing with others, you should join a _____ .

5. **If** there is _____ , little can be achieved.

 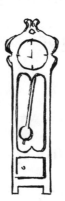 

6. **If** you mix certain substances in _____ class, be sure to watch out—there could be a big bang.

7. **If** something is _____ , it is different from everything else.

8. **If** Mrs. Yin's clock is a hundred years old, it must be an _____ .

9. **If** something is made of _____ , it should last a long time.

The Concert

Remember the saying "It's all Greek to me" from Lesson 2? If something is "all Greek to you," it means that you do not understand it. However, did you know that many of the words that we use every day have come to us from Greek words? For example, some words that have the **k** sound for **ch**, such as *chorus,* come to us from ancient Greece.

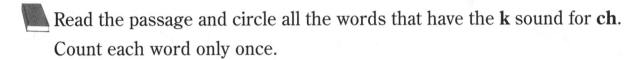 Read the passage and circle all the words that have the **k** sound for **ch**. Count each word only once.

The Christopher family decided to go to a concert. Christine's favorite pop star was singing as well as a group that Charles liked.

Everyone enjoyed the concert, except for Mr. Christopher. He got a headache and went to sleep. But he quickly woke up when the brass instruments sounded some very loud chords.

A small chorus, an orchestra, and some dancers backed up Christine's favorite singer. The dancers' steps were well choreographed and fun to watch. Charles's choral group sang and a guitar played with them.

It was quite chaotic when the concert ended because there were so many people. They all agreed it had been a unique concert. Mr. Christopher had to admit that once he got used to the music, he began to enjoy it too.

➔ Did you find the 9 words with the **k** sound for **ch**?

Did you figure out what "choreographed" means?

It means

(a) rhythmic and fast.

(b) the planning of steps and movements of a dance.

What Is It?
Echinoderms

What are echinoderms?

(a) fish   (b) insects   (c) sea animals

 Read the passage to find out.

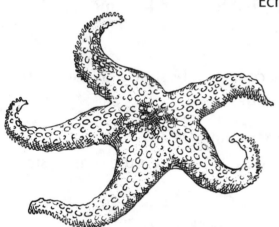

Echinoderms (i-ki'-nə-dərms) are animals that live in the sea. They are not fish, as some people think. *Echinoderm* means "spiny-skinned" in the Greek language. Their bodies are covered with spines and are round and star shaped. Echinoderms have 5 or more arms and a central body.

Echinoderms do not have a head, but they do have a mouth, an opening called the central disk, to eat with. They have systems to digest food and reproduce. They also have two unique features. They have structures called "tube feet" with pads on the bottom that help them move slowly. Also, if an echinoderm's arm or a part of its body is broken off or eaten by a fish, it will usually grow back again.

Echinoderms are important to sea life. Some of them recycle food by feeding on dead and decaying materials. There are over 500 different kinds of echinoderms, including starfish, sea cucumbers, sea urchins, and sea lilies.

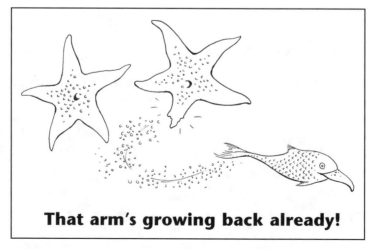

That arm's growing back already!

➜ Circle the correct answer.

1. Echinoderms live

    (a) on land.

    (b) in the sea.

2. Echinoderms are given this name because they have

    (a) bodies covered with spines.

    (b) structures called tube feet.

3. Echinoderms have

    (a) large heads.

    (b) no heads.

4. A unique characteristic of echinoderms is

    (a) they can regrow an arm or a part of the body.

    (b) they can change their shape.

5. There are

    (a) a few kinds of echinoderms.

    (b) many kinds of echinoderms.

6. One kind of echinoderm is

    (a) a worm.

    (b) a starfish.

7. Because some echinoderms eat dead and decaying material, they are

    (a) bad for sea life.

    (b) important for sea life.

What Is It?
Arachnids

(a) insects   (b) a group of animals that includes spiders

 Read the passage to find out.

 There are more than 100,000 different kinds of arachnids (a-rak'-nids), a group of animals that include spiders, scorpions, mites, ticks, and daddy longlegs. Arachnids may have been the first creatures to live on land. Most of them have a way of killing their prey with poison. They live mainly on land, although a few mites and spiders live in water.

Arachnids are not insects. Insects have three body parts and six legs. Arachnids are divided into two parts: the head region and the abdomen. They have four pairs of legs on the front half of their bodies.

A unique feature of arachnids is their respiratory system. They breathe through tiny openings called spiracles, which are on the sides of their bodies. Air passes from the spiracles to hollow sacs with leaflike structures on the abdomen. These structures are called "book lungs" because they look like the pages in a book.

Spiders and daddy longlegs are useful because they eat many kinds of harmful insects and pests such as flies. Some arachnids can be harmful to people. Scorpions can kill with their poison. Mites can damage fruit crops. Ticks are dangerous because they can pass on diseases.

→ Circle the correct answer.

1. Which is an arachnid?

(a) a crab

(b) a spider

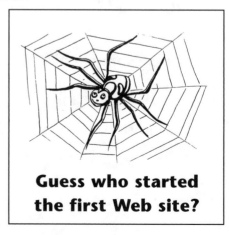

Guess who started the first Web site?

2. Most arachnids kill their prey by

    (a) poisoning them.

    (b) crushing them.

3. The bodies of arachnids are divided into

    (a) 2 parts.

    (b) 3 parts.

4. The unique feature of arachnids is their

    (a) digestive system.

    (b) respiratory system.

5. The respiratory system has to do with

    (a) eating.

    (b) breathing.

6. Arachnids take in air through their

    (a) book lungs.

    (b) leaves.

7. Spiders and daddy longlegs are useful because

    (a) they eat dead materials.

    (b) they eat pests such as flies.

8. Some arachnids cause harm to

    (a) people because they pass on diseases.

    (b) water because they poison it.

Spider Stories

For some reason, many people are fascinated with spiders. They appear in the legends, myths and folk tales of many different cultures. For example, in Native American Navajo folklore, there is a wise, old Spider Woman who has magical powers and teaches weaving. The Navajo have protected spiders, and in the old days, spiders' webs were rubbed on the arms of baby girls so that they will become good weavers.

In Greek mythology, there is a well-known spider story from which spiders got their name, *arachnids*. This is a story about the boastful girl named Arachne (ə-rak´-nē).

Arachne

What do you think Arachne boasts about? Circle the answer you think is correct.

(a) her lovely, unique voice   (b) her beauty   (c) her skillful weaving

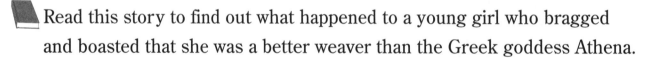

Read this story to find out what happened to a young girl who bragged and boasted that she was a better weaver than the Greek goddess Athena.

In the olden days, all cloth was woven by hand. The young girl Arachne became an expert. She made beautiful fabric with lovely, colorful designs. Everyone agreed she was very skillful.

"Yes, I know I am good," she said. "I am the best weaver in the world," she boasted.

"You are lucky the gods gave you such a wonderful talent," people said.

She replied, "The gods didn't give me anything. I learned this on my own. They can't teach me anything, not even Athena."

The goddess Athena was known for her great skill in weaving, as well as her great wisdom, so Arachne was asking for trouble. You do not challenge gods.

Naturally, Athena was told about the young upstart Arachne. She was furious.

"I will teach that girl a lesson," she said to herself, and she began to plot what she would do.

A few days later, Arachne was busy weaving, as usual. She noticed a shadow fall across her work. She looked up and saw an old woman watching her.

"Good, isn't it?" bragged Arachne.

"Yes, it's very nice—for a human," replied the old woman.

"What do you mean, for a human? It's better than anyone could do, including the gods, even that goddess Athena!"

"Really!" exclaimed the old woman. "You think you are better than Athena?"

"No doubt about it. My work is much better than hers."

"We will see about that," the old woman said. In a flash she threw off her cloak to reveal who she was—Athena!

Arachne was shocked and afraid. It was one thing to brag about being better than a goddess, but quite a different matter to come face-to-face with that goddess. But it was too late.

"I challenge you to a contest," declared Athena, and, of course, Arachne had to accept the challenge.

The two worked side by side on their looms. Arachne produced a very lovely pattern, beautifully woven. However, Athena's work was much more colorful and the pattern more complicated. The weaving was a masterpiece. It was obvious which one was the best.

"You are too full of yourself, by far," Athena told Arachne. "For this you will suffer. You can continue to weave, but from now on you will be a _____.

→ What did Arachne turn into? Write the answer on the line above.

What did Arachne boast about? Circle the correct answer.

(a) her lovely, unique voice   (b) her beauty   c) her skillful weaving

Kwaku-Ananse

How do you think two small spiders could outwit the most dangerous animals of the jungle?

 This spider story is about Kwaku-Ananse, a trickster spider. The story comes from West Africa.

Kwaku-Ananse (Kwa-koo'-A-nahn'-zā) was a spider. He was a very confident spider, very sure of himself. To tell the truth, he was rather full of himself. He believed he could achieve whatever he wanted. Kwaku-Ananse admired Nyankonpon (Nə-yän'-kän'pän), the sky god, because he was a wonderful storyteller. Nyankonpon had made up some very unique tales and Kwaku-Ananse wanted them.

Kwaku-Ananse went to Nyankonpon and told him, "I want to buy your stories."

"Not for sale," replied Nyankonpon. "At least, not for the price you could pay me. Not even the richest man could pay the price they deserve."

"What is the price they deserve?" asked Kwaku-Ananse, full of himself.

Nyankonpon rubbed his chin thoughtfully. "Well, let me see. You would have to bring me Onini (O-nē'-nē), the python; Osebo (O-sā'-bō), the leopard; Mmoboro (Mə-bau'-rō), the hornet bees; and Mmoatia (Mwa-tē'-a), the spirit," Nyankonpon replied. He knew it would be impossible for Kwaku-Ananse to capture such fierce animals.

"It's a deal. I will bring you all of them," said Kwaku-Ananse.

Nyankonpon smiled and said, "Fine, I will be here waiting for them."

Kwaku-Ananse crawled off purposefully. He was so confident he could capture all the animals that he began to hum a little tune.

"It should not be too difficult," he murmured to himself. "I just need to tackle them one by one. I'll start with Onini."

When Kwaku-Ananse got home he told his wife, Aso (A-sō'), what he had to do. Aso offered to help. She said the best way to catch Onini the python was to get a branch from a palm tree and a length of vine. So the two of them went off and got these. But when Aso saw the branch from the palm tree that Kwaku-Ananse had cut she told him it was not long enough.

"It's plenty long enough," Kwaku-Ananse replied irritably.

"No, it's not," said Aso. And the two began to argue. Their loud voices attracted Onini, who squirmed out from under some leaves.

"What's going on?" he asked. "You woke me up from a nice, quiet snooze."

"Aso says the palm branch is not as long as you," said Kwaku-Ananse.

"We can soon see who is right," said Onini. He stretched himself on top of the leaf—and yes, you can guess what happened. Ananse quickly wrapped the leaf around him and tied him up with the vine.

"One done, three to go," Kwaku-Ananse shouted with glee.

Osebo was the next on the list, so Kwaku-Ananse asked Aso if she had any good techniques for capturing a leopard. She told him to dig a big hole between Osebo's lair, or den, and the stream and to cover it with leaves. Sure enough, there was Osebo at the bottom of the hole the next day, trying to get out.

"Two down, two to go," Kwaku-Anase said with satisfaction.

The next animals on the list were Mmoboro, the hornets. Now Kwaku-Ananse was not too excited about catching them because they had such nasty stings. But they had to be caught if he was to get the stories, so once again he asked Aso for her ideas.

Aso told Kwaku-Ananse to get a gourd. A gourd is a fruit with a hard skin that can be hollowed out to make a container.

Next, Aso told him to fill the gourd with water. Then she told him to pour half of the water on the hornets, which were hanging from a nearby tree, and half on his head.

Kwaku-Ananse did this. Then he put a large leaf from a plantain (like a banana) on his head and called out to the hornets.

"Hey, you guys. Look, it's raining. Why don't you come under my plantain leaf to get out of the wet?"

As the hornets flew down, Kwaku-Ananse captured them in the gourd and trapped them inside with the plantain leaf.

"Wow, this is great! I've only Mmoatia to catch," said Kwaku-Ananse to Aso.

Kwaku-Ananse and Aso had to give a lot of thought to catching Mmoatia because spirits were not like animals. They never stayed in one place for long. They were there one minute, but the next minute they were gone.

The two crafty spiders carved a doll from a piece of wood. Next, they covered the doll with sticky gum from a tree. Then they mashed up some yams, or sweet potatoes, which animals, people, and spirits all loved to eat. They put the yams into a wooden bowl and set it among the trees where the spirits often played.

Mmoatia came to play later that day.

"Oh, yummy, yams," she cried out. "Can I help myself?" she asked the doll who was standing beside the bowl, obviously protecting it.

When the doll did not reply, Mmoatia slapped the doll. Her hand stuck to the sticky gum that covered the doll. She slapped it again with the other hand, and that hand stuck, too.

"Got you!" cried Kwaku-Ananse happily, and he dropped Mmoatia, still stuck to the doll, into a bag.

Kwaku-Ananse went to Nyankonpon, the sky god, and presented him with Onini, the python; Osebo, the leopard; Mmoatia, the hornets; and Mmoboro, the spirit.

"You have done well, yes, very well, Kwaku-Ananse," said Nyankonpon. He was so impressed that he called all the other gods to see what Kwaku-Ananse, the small spider, had accomplished.

"Look at this," he said waving his arm toward Kwaku-Ananse and all the animals he had captured.

"Because Kwaku-Ananse has met all my requirements, I will give him my box of stories. From today on they will be known as Spider Stories!"

And to this day, Kwaku-Ananse and Aso spin their spider stories.

→ Circle the correct answer.

1. What is the lesson of this story?

(a) If you can capture certain animals, you will do well in life.

(b) If you are determined to achieve something, you can achieve it.

2. Kwaku-Ananse admired Nyankonpon because

(a) he was the sky god.

(b) he had made up some unique stories.

3. In which order did Kwaku-Ananse capture the animals?

(a) the leopard, the snake, the spirit, the hornets

(b) the snake, the leopard, the hornets, the spirit

4. The leopard was captured

(a) when he fell into a hole.

(b) when he stretched out on a palm leaf.

5. Kwaku-Ananse used gum to capture

(a) the hornets.

(b) the spirit.

6. To whom did Kwaku-Ananse tell it was raining?

(a) the hornets

(b) the snake

7. Who gave Kwaku-Ananse the ideas for how to capture the animals?

(a) Nyankonpon, the sky god

(b) his wife, Aso

8. Nyankonpon was

(a) angry because he did not expect Kwaku-Ananse to capture all the animals.

(b) impressed that Kwaku-Ananse had accomplished such a difficult task.

✎ Write your own spider story.

_____

_____

_____

_____

_____

_____

_____

_____

_____

_____

_____

_____

_____

_____

_____

_____

_____

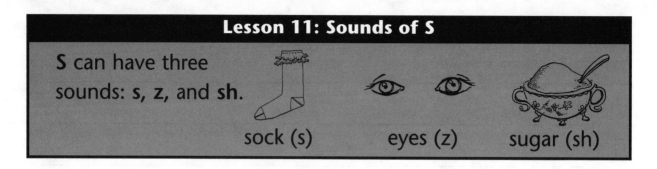

Lesson 11: Sounds of S

S can have three sounds: **s, z,** and **sh.**

sock (s) eyes (z) sugar (sh)

Sound out the letters to read each word.

Notice that the words in red are sight words. They cannot be sounded out, and they do not follow a rule.

s	sun	slice	star	say
	answer	sentence	system	goodness
	said	sew	school	steak
	course	sieve	some	false
z	rose	is	has	news
	cheese	easy	days	faces
	music	because	museum	nose
	busy	yours	does	lose
sh	sure	sugar	tissue	assure
	pressure			

These words have another sound for **s.**

measure	treasure	pleasure	leisure

→ Draw a line between the words that have the same **s** sound.

music inside	please sure	Saturday does
seven was	toes tissue	poison soon
easy theirs	myself eyes	pleasure nose
sugar pressure	present wise	museum treasure

Words can be made up of 3 parts.

a beginning   a middle, main part   an ending

The beginning part of a word is called a **prefix.**

The middle, main part of a word is called a **base word.**

The end part of a word is called a **suffix.**

Look at these words:

sure   **assure**   **surely**

Which word is the base word? _____

Which word has a prefix? _____

Which word has a suffix? _____

→ Use one of the words to complete each sentence.

1. Carmel: "If we finish the assignment before the end of class, I am _____ Mr. Samuels will give us a longer recess."

2. Yoo: "I _____ hope you are right."

3. Mr. Samuels: "Yes, I can _____ you that you will have extra recess time."

➜ Add an **s** to find out what each sentence is saying. On the line write the sound that **s** has: **s, z,** or **sh**.

_____ 1. Isaac had a de___ert supper for the class.

_____ 2. There were so many dishe_ the kids found it hard to decide what to have.

_____ 3. Rosa chose strawberries sprinkled with _ugar.

_____ 4. Jessica helped herself to chee_e.

_____ 5. The others enjoyed cakes, cookie_, and pies.

_____ 6. A CD played mu_ic while everyone ate.

_____ 7. As they watched a movie, Sarah up_et her glass of soda.

_____ 8. Isaac gave her some ti___ues to wipe up the spill.

_____ 9. The others a___ured her that no harm was done.

→ Put an X in the box next to the sentence that tells about the picture.

☐ Stella goes hiking in her leisure time.

☐ Gustavo listens to music when he does his homework.

☐ The class went on a trip to the museum.

☐ The clown made faces at the circus.

☐ Serena was sweating from doing thirty push-ups.

☐ Sandra needed tissues because she was sneezing.

☐ Samantha always puts slices of banana with sugar on her cereal.

☐ Sidney never puts sugar on his cereal.

→ Read the saying in bold print. Then put an X next to the sentence that explains its meaning.

1. One good turn deserves another.

☐ If you turn one way, you should then turn the other way.

☐ If you wait your turn, you will be rewarded.

☐ If you are helpful to someone, someone is likely to help you.

2. It's time to face the music.

☐ You can now enjoy the music.

☐ You can look at the music if you are not sure of it.

☐ You need to accept the results, no matter now unpleasant.

3. Don't count your chickens before they're hatched.

☐ When you get home from the market, check to be sure that the eggs have not hatched.

☐ You should wait for a chicken's eggs to hatch.

☐ Don't count on something until it's actually happened.

4. All that glitters is not gold.

☐ The sun shines but it is not made of gold.

☐ Things are not always what they seem to be.

☐ You can buy fake jewelry.

Lesson 11: The Sh Sound

Several letters can make the **sh sound: sh, ci/ti,** and **sion/tion.**

shell   glacier   addition

Sound out the letters to read each word.

sh	ship	shout	shoe	shears
	shadow	shake	short	shiver
	shower	shy	shoulder	shine
ci/ti	special	delicious	patient	ancient
	crucial	species	sufficient	patience
	efficient	precious	conscious	gracious

sion/tion   Words with this ending have the sound of **shun.**

action	fiction	admission	motion
session	addition	expression	invention
permission	mention	nation	admission

→ Choose the correct ending for each word and write the ending on the line.

ac_____ cial	suffi_____ cient	expres_____ cial
cru_____ tion	inven_____ tion	spe_____ sion
fic_____ tient	mo_____ cious	permis_____ sion
pa_____ tion	gra_____ tion	deli_____ cious

Wompo the Wallaby

A wallaby is a type of

    (a) cat   (b) kangaroo   (c) monkey

Where does a wallaby live?

    (a) Africa   (b) Asia   (c) Australia

 Read Wompo the Wallaby's interview with a reporter to find out.

I'm a reporter and my **mission** is to write about wallabies for the magazine *Animal Watch.* I'm excited because I have never met a wallaby, and I have never been to Australia where wallabies live.

I was lucky to catch up with Wompo the Wallaby on my first day, because wallabies usually come out to feed when it's dark. Also, I was told that they are not very friendly. But Wompo was quite talkative and **patient** as I asked him many questions during our **session** together.

"Wallabies are **special** to Australia," Wompo said. "We live mainly in south-eastern Australia and the nearby island of Tasmania. We belong to the kangaroo **species,** so we are marsupials." He repeated mar-soo-pē-əls slowly for me to make sure I got it right.

"I'm called a red-necked wallaby. I'll let you figure out the reason for that! I have lots of relatives who are like me with slight **variations.** I am two-and-a-half-feet tall, which is smaller than a kangaroo," he said, peering at me to make sure I was paying attention.

"We red-neckers can't climb trees like our cousins, the kangaroos. We bound along the ground. Fortunately, we have very strong hind legs, and we can hop like no one else. When we are in **motion,** we can travel as fast as 40 miles an hour." And Wompo bounded off to give me a **demonstration.**

He returned with no signs of **exhaustion**, ready to run off again. I am discovering that wallabies are not only **special** to Australia—they are just very **special**.

→ Checking up: See if you are learning all the details about wallabies. Circle the correct answer.

1. What is a wallaby?

    (a) a cat

    (b) a kangaroo

    (c) a monkey

2. Where does a wallaby live?

    (a) Africa

    (b) Asia

    (c) Australia

3. Wallabies usually can be found

    (a) during the day.

    (b) when it is dark.

4. Wallabies are

    (a) bigger than kangaroos.

    (b) smaller than kangaroos.

5. Unlike its cousins, the kangaroos, wallabies cannot

    (a) climb trees.

    (b) hop very fast.

6. *Bound* means

    (a) to slide and glide.

    (b) to move with leaps.

Wompo told me that he was especially proud of his tail. "You must agree it is a wonderful invention. It is slender and elegant. It gives us **graciousness.** And it is very useful. It stretches out horizontally when I run to give me balance. In addition, it supports me when I am standing. It is also a **crucial** way we let each other know if there is danger." He showed me how he did this by thumping his tail on the ground.

Wompo gave me an invitation to come to his home in an area of small shrubs and trees. "It's no **mansion**, but it's comfortable. And it's very con-venient to the grasses, leaves, and herbs we like to eat," he said as he munched on a leaf and sighed with satisfaction. "Now that's what I call good **nutrition!**" he announced.

"I **mentioned** that we are marsupials," Wompo continued. "That means our babies grow inside the mother's pouch. We also have two stomachs, but apart from that we are very similar to you. We have the same **efficient** systems that you have. No, we're not that different from you," he said with an amused **expression** on his face.

Wompo decided he had done enough talking. "Got to be going," he said, and off he leaped into the bushes. I had enjoyed meeting this special animal.

→ Circle the correct answer,

1. Wompo was especially proud of his

    (a) red color.

    (b) tail.

2. What do wallabies use to warn of danger?

    (a) their hind legs

    (b) their tails

3. Wallabies eat

    (a) grasses, leaves, and herbs.

    (b) small animals.

4. Baby wallabies grow

    (a) in their mother's pouch.

    (b) on their mother's back.

5. Wallabies have

    (a) one stomach like humans.

    (b) two stomachs.

6. Divide marsupials into syllables:_____

→ Reread the story. Notice the **sh** words in bold print. Did they make sense to you? Match the words with their meanings.

_____ 1. mission	(a) different; not like others	
_____ 2. patient	(b) a meeting	
_____ 3. session	(c) can wait calmly without complaining	
_____ 4. special	(d) a special task	

_____ 1. species	(a) movement	
_____ 2. variations	(b) the act of showing	
_____ 3. motion	(c) differences	
_____ 4. demonstration	(d) a group that is alike in some ways	

→ Choose one of the above words to complete each sentence.

1. Jamal waited _____ly until his mom came back from jogging.

2. The secret agent's _____ was to find the lost instructions.

3. Tigers and lions are two different _____ of cat.

4. Andrea played several _____ of the tune on the violin.

5. The class paid careful attention to Mr. Kin's _____ of how a battery works.

6. "Congress is in _____" said the sign.

7. The rocking _____ of the boat made Natasha seasick.

8. Martha has a very _____ voice and can sing all the high notes.

➜ Match these words with their meanings.

____ 1. exhaustion	(a) a large house
____ 2. graciousness	(b) great tiredness
____ 3. crucial	(c) a kind, charming way of behaving
____ 4. mansion	(d) most important; necessary

____ 1. nutrition	(a) to speak about
____ 2. mention	(b) food; how the body makes use of food to grow
____ 3. efficient	(c) a look that shows how one feels
____ 4. expression	(d) doing something with the least amount of time and effort

➜ Choose one of the above words to complete each sentence.

1. Henry Ford's method of producing cars on an assembly line was very _____ because the cars were all the same.

2. "Did I _____ to you that I have a practice after school?" asked Olga.

3. Sergio had been running for over ten miles, and his fall in the race was due to _____.

4. Emily shot the _____ goal that won the team the championship.

5. The _____ was now divided into several apartments.

6. An example of Monica's _____ is her caring, pleasant way of speaking.

7. The class had to make posters on _____ to show what a healthy diet should be.

8. Jasper had a sad _____ on his face when he told Ruby that his dog had died.

Three Ancient Civilizations of the Americas

Our rich heritage comes from ancestors from many different cultures. Many of the important, ancient cultures that have shaped our world are from Latin America. In the next three passages, you will find out about the history of three ancient and powerful Indian civilizations in Central and South America. Who were they? How can you tell that they valued learning, art and religion?

 Locate the three groups on the map and then read about their civilizations.

The Maya

Who were the Maya? What happened to them?

 It was more than 1,500 years ago that the Maya (Mi'-yə) Indians created a society in the jungles of Central America and what is now southern Mexico. Here, in the dense forest, they carefully planned and built cities with beautiful, tall buildings made of stone. They also built great religious centers of huge stone pyramids with richly decorated temples.

The Maya were very well organized. They developed a government and a system of laws. They were also extremely religious. The most respected people were the priests. These were learned men as well as religious leaders. They invented a method of writing that used pictures and symbols. They also created a system of mathematics. They studied the stars, the moon, and the sun, and from this they invented a calendar that was more accurate than any calendar in Europe at that time.

The Mayas were also skillful craftsmen, making beautiful objects in stone and creating handsome jewelry and masks.

The Maya society reached its peak between 200 and 800 A.D. Then it declined. No one knows why.

Three Ancient Civilizations of the Americas

→ Circle the region where the Maya lived on the map on page 169.

→ Circle the correct answer.

1. The Maya created a society

    (a) in the mountains.

    (b) in the jungles.

2. The Maya built tall buildings made of

    (a) stone.

    (b) wood.

3. The Maya built

    (a) large shopping centers.

    (b) huge religious centers.

4. The educated people were

    (a) the men.

    (b) the priests.

5. The Maya invented a writing system that was based on

    (a) pictures and symbols.

    (b) the sounds of language.

6. From studying the stars, moon, and sun, the Maya invented

    (a) a system of mathematics.

    (b) an accurate calendar.

7. The Maya civilization disappeared

    (a) because they were conquered.

    (b) and no one knows why.

The Aztecs

Who were the Aztecs? What made their capital unique?

The Aztecs were wandering hunters who settled in present-day Mexico in the 1200s. They were powerful and developed trained armies. They conquered other Indian groups. Eventually, they ruled more than 5 million people.

Like the Maya, the Aztecs (Az'-teks) were well organized and built well-planned cities. The Aztec capital, Tenochtitlán (Te-noch-te-tlahn'), became one of the largest cities in the world at that time. It was unique because it was built on an island in a lake. This was to prevent enemies from attacking it. Tenochtitlán became modern-day Mexico City.

Tenochtitlán had great government buildings, pyramids, temples, and beautiful parks. It also had busy marketplaces and houses. Causeways (raised roads) connected the city to the mainland. Canals brought fresh water to the city. The Aztecs developed their own form of writing and an accurate calendar. They worshipped many gods, but the gods of the sun and war were the most important.

The Aztecs became powerful and rich. They began to demand payments from the other Indian people they had conquered. This made these groups hate the Aztecs. Later, this hatred led to the defeat of the Aztecs, because the conquered people joined with the Spanish to overcome them.

→ Circle the region where the Aztecs lived on the map on page 169.

→ Circle the correct answer.

1. The Aztecs were originally

    (a) farmers.

    (b) hunters.

2. The Aztecs conquered the neighboring Indian people because

    (a) they were smarter.

    (b) they had trained armies.

3. Tenochtitlán was a unique city because

    (a) it was built in the jungle.

    (b) it was built on an island in a lake.

4. Causeways are

    (a) raised roads.

    (b) waterways.

5. The Aztecs were able to record important events in their history because

    (a) they passed down events by word of mouth to each generation.

    (b) they developed a form of writing.

6. The Aztecs became rich from the payments they demanded from the people they conquered. How could this have hurt them later on?

    (a) The conquered groups hated the Aztecs and joined with the Spanish to defeat their rulers.

    (b) The Aztecs became so wealthy they became lazy and could no longer control the conquered people.

The Incas

Who were the Incas? What two resources did they have that the Spanish conquerors wanted?

Farther south, along the western coast of South America, lived another powerful and remarkable group of Native Americans. Like the Aztecs, the Incas (In'-kəs) developed a vast empire by conquering neighboring Indians.

The Incas worshipped the sun. They believed that their leader, the Inca, came from the sun. He was an all-powerful ruler. His subjects obeyed whatever he demanded. The Inca would not put up with laziness. Everyone was expected to work. Most of his subjects were required to spend part of their time on public projects for the empire. They built roads, tunnels, and bridges through the Andes Mountains to connect distant parts of the empire. They built temples and terraces. They mined silver and gold. In return for their labor, the subjects received help when they became old or sick.

The Incas had a highly organized government. They were also skillful farmers. They grew corn, white and sweet potatoes, squash, tomatoes, and peanuts. They created ways to make full use of the dry and barren land and the mountains. They developed irrigation systems to water their crops, and they cut terraces into the steep mountainsides to create flat fields.

The Incas were expert builders. Like the Egyptians, they moved heavy loads without the use of the wheel. With the help of llamas (camel-like animals), they managed to move huge blocks of stone over long distances and to build large structures of stone slabs. These slabs were so perfectly cut that they didn't require mortar—and they still stand today.

The Incas were remarkable people. They were hardworking and inventive. One-third of their land was dry desert, one-third mountains and valleys, and one-third jungle. From this, they created a successful and strong society. The land had one good feature: It was rich in silver and gold. However, this turned out to be fatal for the Incas because the Spaniards desired these valuable resources and conquered the Incas to get them.

➜ Circle the region where the Incas lived on the map on page 169.

➜ Circle the correct answer.

1. The Incas lived

   (a) north of the Aztecs.

   (b) south of the Aztecs.

2. The Incas worshipped

   (a) the sun.

   (b) the moon.

3. The Incas would not tolerate

   (a) people working too hard.

   (b) laziness.

4. In return for building bridges, roads, and other public projects, the Incas

   (a) received payment for their work.

   (b) got help when they were old and sick.

5. The Incas were able to farm the steep mountainsides by

   (a) cutting terraces to create flat areas.

   (b) covering the mountains with soil.

6. The land of the Incas was difficult to farm, but it had two useful resources. One of these was

   (a) diamonds.

   (b) silver.

The Clever Son of the Sun God

The Incas developed a large empire by defeating neighboring Indians. But there was one group, the Chimus, which would not give in to them. The Incas made them surrender their kingdom without even a fight. How did they do this?

 Read the story to find out.

The Incas had gradually conquered their Indians neighbors and were becoming the largest empire in the Americas. They had taken **possession** of most of the Andes Mountains and the tropical forests. Now they wanted to take over the desert region between the mountains and the ocean. It was harder than they thought. The Chimu Indians lived there, and they were not about to give up their land to the Incas.

After several unsuccessful raids into Chimu land, the Inca leaders went to the Inca, their ruler, to seek his advice.

"First, we must talk to them. We must warn them that they will come to no good if they continue to **resist** us," said the Inca.

The Inca called several of his trusted messengers and sent them off to the Chimus.

When the messengers did not return, the Inca became angry. He decided he would lead his men himself against the Chimus.

When they arrived at the walls of the city where the Great Chimu, the leader, lived, the Inca ordered his men to climb the walls and attack. But as soon as they placed their ladders against the walls, the Chimus knocked them down.

The Inca saw that this method of attack was not successful. So he called his men together and told them to rest. Then he went off alone to think. An idea came to him. What do you think the idea was?

➜ Checking up: See if you are following the story. Circle the correct answer.

1. The Incas had conquered most of the Andes Mountains and tropical forest regions.

   (a) yes

   (b) no

2. The land between the mountains was

   (a) rich and fertile.

   (b) desert.

3. When the Incas could not defeat the Chimus, the Inca ruler told his men that

   (a) they must fight more fiercely.

   (b) someone must talk to the Chimus.

4. The messengers

   (a) did not return.

   (b) said the Chimus would not give up their land.

5. The Chimu city was protected by

   (a) water.

   (b) a wall.

6. The Inca stopped his men from attacking because

   (a) they were tired.

   (b) he wanted to think.

The Inca's idea had to do with water. Without water, the Chimus would die. And where did their water come from? It came from the Andes Mountains, which the Incas controlled.

The next day the Chimus were amazed to see the Inca soldiers retreating. Had they won so easily, they wondered. They waited several days, but there was no sign of their enemy, so they went back to their normal lives.

Meanwhile, the Inca sent his soldiers up into the mountains to change the flow of water that went into the pipes that carried the water to the Chimus.

When the soldiers had done this, the Inca returned to the walls of the Chimu city. He blew a horn and demanded that the Great Chimu come out and speak to him. The Great Chimu came to the ledge of the high wall. He shone in his golden crown and robes. He was amazed to see the Inca standing all by himself.

"I am the Inca, son of the Sun God. I have power over the air and water. I have taken your water from you and will not return it until you surrender your kingdom."

The Great Chimu laughed. He turned his back on the Inca, and disappeared.

The Great Chimu did not laugh for long. All too soon the supply of water dried up and the people became weak from thirst. The Great Chimu knew he was defeated. He gave up his kingdom to the Inca without even a fight.

➔ Circle the correct answer.

The Incas made the Chimus surrender without even a fight by

    (a) capturing the Great Chimu.

    (b) cutting off the Chimus's water supply.

The sun was important in the lives of the Incas. They created many stories about the sun. Make up your own story about the sun.

_____

_____

_____

_____

_____

_____

_____

_____

_____

_____

_____

_____

_____

_____

Lesson 12: Vowels with R

When vowels are followed by **r**, they have an **unexpected** sound.

ear   swarm   worm

Sound out the letters to read each word.

ear   **Earth** has the same sound as **er, ir**, and **ur**.

earth	search	heard
learn	early	earn
pearl	earnest	yearn

wor   In most words that begin with **wor, or** has the **er, ir, ur** sound.

word	work	world
worse	worst	worry
worth	worthy	worship

ar   When **ar** follows **w, ar** can have the **or** sound.

war	warm	toward
warn	award	reward
inward	wardrobe	awkward
warrior	backward	swarm

These words have the **or** sound: quart, quarter, quartz.

→ Draw a line between the words that have the same **vowel** with **r** sound.

warm	search	worst	warrior
learn	world	early	work
worth	toward	warn	heard
pearl	swarm	quart	earn
worthy	worry	worst	award
awkward	yearn	earth	worm

→ Underline each base word. Then write the base word under the correct heading.

wordless	searched	relearn
inward	working	warned
earthly	quarterly	worthy

er, ir, ur sound   **er, ir, ur** sound   **or** sound

_____   _____   _____

_____   _____   _____

_____   _____   _____

→ Choose one of the words from the list to answer each riddle. Write the word on the line. Cross out the words as you use them.

search	**words**	**yearn**	**award**	**quarter**	**worm**
backward	**swarm**	**warm**	**earth**	**worst**	**reward**

1. Another word meaning "world": _____

2. It is like a prize: _____

3. A lot of bees or insects: _____

4. An early bird might have one for breakfast: _____

5. They make up a sentence: _____

6. The opposite of "best": _____

7. Something given in return for a good deed: _____

8. To want something badly: _____

9. The opposite of "forward": _____

10. Not cool and not hot: _____

11. You do this when you have lost something: _____

12. It is one-fourth: _____

→ Match the sayings with their meanings.

_____ 1. The early bird catches the worm.

_____ 2. down to earth

(a) If you get there near the beginning, you will get what you want.

(b) practical, sensible

→ Draw a line to the correct ending of each sentence.

___1. Raymond cut the oranges   into the bowl.

___2. He put the quarters   over them.

___3. Then he poured a quart of juice   into quarters.

___4. Susan was doing her homework   for dinner

___5. She was learning about   in her room.

___6. She worried that she would not finish in time   earthworms.

___7. Mr. Wardman left work   early.

___8. He went to the gym   dinner.

___9. Then he had an early   to work out.

___10. Divers in Japan search   for their skill.

___11. They are rewarded by selling them   for pearls.

___12. They are known throughout the world   for high prices.

How Things Work
Watch It! Television

How does a TV work?

 Read the passage and answer the questions. Then circle the one word with the **ear, wor,** or **war** sound.

The picture you see and the sounds you hear on TV are sent to you through the air like invisible messages. A camera turns the pictures into electric signals. A microphone picks up the sounds, which are also turned into electric signals. These signals are picked up by your TV antenna and sent to your TV set.

 Here's how it works. When you turn on your TV, you turn the signals in the wired back of your TV into pictures and sound. The picture you see on the screen is actually built up in horizontal lines. On a color television, each line is made of red, green, and blue stripes. Your eye blends together the stripes, and you are rewarded with a sharp, color picture on your screen.

→ Circle the correct answer.

1. How are the picture and words transmitted to you?

    (a) by the wind

    (b) by electric signals

2. What does the antenna do?

    (a) traps the wind

    (b) picks up the electronic signals

3. Turning on the TV

    (a) turns the signals into pictures and sound.

    (b) starts the antenna working.

Watch It! Digital Watches

Read the passage and answer the questions. See if you can find the 13 **ear, wor,** and **war** words. Count each word, even if it is repeated.

Mr. Wentworth always worried that he would not be on time. The worst thing that could happen to him was to be late. But he never was. In fact, he was awarded a plaque for always getting to work so early. He was the only person in the company worthy of such an honor.

One day, however, the very worst thing happened. Mr. Wentworth's beloved watch fell out of his pocket and broke.

Word got around the office, and Mr. Wentworth was given a new watch. But this one was a digital watch. Mr. Wentworth missed winding up his watch each night, because a digital watch does not have to be wound.

Why don't you have to wind a digital watch? This is how it works.

Counter

1. Power from a small battery sends electricity to a tiny quartz crystal. Electrical messages go along the wires inside the clock.

2. A digital watch keeps accurate time because the power sent through the battery makes the crystal shake at a very fast and even speed. A microchip slows down this fast rate to exactly one signal a second.

3. An electronic counter keeps track of the signals and sends a message to the watch face.

→ Circle the correct answer.

1. A digital watch

(a) needs to be wound.

(b) does not need to be wound.

2. What sends electricity to the quartz crystal?

(a) an electronic counter

(b) a battery

3. What does the electricity make the quartz do?

(a) rotate

(b) shake

4. What does the electronic counter do?

(a) It counts how many times the quartz crystal shakes.

(b) It makes the quartz crystal shake.

5. The counter can keep track of how many times the crystal shakes because

(a) the crystal shakes very fast.

(b) the crystal shakes at an even speed.

6. Which is more accurate in keeping time?

(a) a regular watch

(b) a digital watch

The Earthworm

An earthworm does not look a bit like you, but it has some systems that are similar to yours on the inside. Which do you think these are? Circle the answer you think is correct.

(a) the digestive system

(b) the nervous system

(c) the circulatory system

(d) all of these

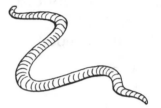

 Read the passage to find out.

The earthworm's home, as its name suggests, is in the soil. When an earthworm comes out of the soil and is above ground, it is in danger. It can dry out in the hot sun, be eaten by a swift, swooping bird, or used as bait by someone who likes to fish.

The earthworm is made up of many segments, or parts, that allow it to wriggle and squirm along the ground and dig through the soil. You may be surprised to learn that it has organs and body systems that are similar to yours.

The earthworm has a mouth to pull in its food and a digestive system with a food tube from its mouth to a hole at the end of its body. It has special body parts and an intestine like our own to break down food and digest and store it.

The earthworm has a complete circulatory system with arteries, veins, and capillaries. It also has a nervous system with a "brain" in the head area and a nerve cord along the lower side of its body.

It has both male and female reproductive organs and mates with other worms. However, some worms can reproduce by splitting in half.

Earthworms play an important role in keeping the soil in good condition. As they burrow, or dig through the soil, they make a network of spaces that let in air and water, which helps the water drain out of the soil. Worms eat a lot of dirt and enrich the soil by breaking down the decaying matter and adding their waste products to the soil.

→ Circle the correct answer.

1. Which systems of the earthworm are similar to ours?

(a) the digestive system

(b) the nervous system

(c) the circulatory system

(d) all of these

2. The earthworm lives in the soil because

(a) it is a nice quiet world down there.

(b) the soil provides food, hides it from its enemies, and keeps it from drying out.

3. The earthworm is more likely to be eaten by

(a) a snake.

(b) a bird.

Why doesn't he leave it to me?

4. The earthworm takes in food in by

(a) absorbing it through its skin.

(b) pulling it into its mouth.

5. The earthworm has a circulatory system similar to ours, with arteries, veins and capillaries.

(a) true

(b) false

6. Earthworms are useful because

(a) they help to keep the soil in good condition.

(b) they eat weeds.

Does the Early Bird Catch the Worm?

> This is a poem about an earthworm. What do you think happens to it?

(a) It is eaten by a bird.   (b) It is not eaten by a bird.

Read the first three stanzas of the poem. Notice that each stanza is made up of four lines.

Early One Morning

It was early on a warm summer's day.

The world was still and happy that way.

A tiny head popped up out of the ground,

Searching and listening for a strange sound.

It looked this way and that for signs of danger,

A passing enemy, a friend, or stranger.

All was clear, so it slowly wriggled out,

Glad to be alive and out and about.

Tired from its work, churning the soil,

It curled into a round, soft coil.

Enjoying the fresh air, it fell asleep,

And what nearly happened could make you weep.

➜ Reread the first three stanzas. Notice how words often rhyme in poems. Underline the rhyming words. Then write them on the lines.

Stanza 1: _____   _____

_____   _____

Stanza 2: _____   _____

_____   _____

Stanza 3: _____   _____

_____   _____

Up in a tree a bird was perched.

For a tasty breakfast she had searched.

But nothing caught the bird's eye, until

She spied the juicy morsel, lying so still.

The eager bird quickly flew down to eat,

But what an awkward surprise she did meet.

A swarm of noisy bees came buzzing past.

They woke up the worm, which disappeared, fast!

➔ What happened to the worm? Circle the correct answer.

    (a) It was eaten by a bird

    (b) It was saved by a swarm of bees.

✎ Write a poem about an earthworm. Choose colorful, descriptive words and some rhyming words.

_____

_____

_____

_____

_____

_____

_____

_____

_____

_____

_____

_____

_____

_____

_____

_____

Lesson 13: Syllables

When a word has a prefix or a suffix, divide the word between the base word and the prefix and suffix.	turn-ing slow-ly
When a word ends in **le** with a consonant before it, divide the word **before** the consonant.	can-dle tur-tle
When a word ends in **ckle**, divide the word between **k** and **le**.	tick-le pick-le

→ Circle the vowels. Write the number of vowels in each word. Then write the number of vowel sounds and syllables in the word.

	Vowels	Vowel Sounds and Syllables		Vowels	Vowel Sounds and Syllables
dislike	_____	_____	unlucky	_____	_____
assure	_____	_____	apple	_____	_____
bottle	_____	_____	leisurely	_____	_____
goodness	_____	_____	wrinkle	_____	_____
easy	_____	_____	remeasure	_____	_____
people	_____	_____	little	_____	_____
worker	_____	_____	learning	_____	_____
award	_____	_____	uncle	_____	_____
pickle	_____	_____	surely	_____	_____
working	_____	_____	tackle	_____	_____
rectangle	_____	_____	inward	_____	_____
uneasy	_____	_____	muscle	_____	_____
knuckle	_____	_____	disappear	_____	_____
searching	_____	_____	backward	_____	_____
whistle	_____	_____	twinkle	_____	_____

➜ Read each word and then write it on the line, using hyphens to divide the word into syllables.

reward	_____	sugarless	_____
purple	_____	sicken	_____
falsehood	_____	kindness	_____
eagle	_____	double	_____
worrying	_____	uneasy	_____
mumble	_____	handle	_____
yearly	_____	pickle	_____
toward	_____	earthquake	_____
startle	_____	wooden	_____

➜ Draw a line between the beginning and the end of each word.

chor	ward	tis	sue
awk	gar	wor	robe
eas	us	ward	umn
su	y	col	ship
phy	est	be	ry
cha	sique	wor	nique
earn	os	char	cause
mu	seum	tech	acter

The Boy Who Was Meant to Be King: Part 1

In this British legend, when King Arthur was born, the head of a huge dragon appeared in the sky. Why do you think this happened?

 Read the story to find out.

A very long time ago, Uther led his fellow British lords against fierce invaders and defeated them. The lords were relieved to have such a fine leader and made him their high king, or Pendragon, meaning "Dragon's Head."

A brief time after becoming king, Uther Pendragon fell in love with the beautiful Lady Igraine. In order to win her hand, he asked his advisor, the magician Merlin, to help him. In return, Uther promised he would give Merlin their firstborn son.

Why had Merlin demanded their heir? It was because he was wise and could see into the future. He knew that there were terrible times ahead and that the future king needed to be protected.

Soon after the baby boy was born, Merlin appeared.

"You can't take my baby from me!" cried Queen Igraine. She tried to shield the baby in her arms.

"Believe me, it is for the boy's own good," Merlin assured her.

He took the unhappy parents to the window and pointed to the sky. There they saw a huge dragon's head formed by the stars.

"This is a sign. It is not I who calls for your son, but destiny."

The queen gently gave Merlin the baby boy. A mist formed around him and he disappeared.

The king and queen grieved for their son. Then, within months, the king was poisoned and Britain was plunged into chaos.

→ Checking up: See if you are following the story. Circle the correct answer.

1. The story takes place long ago in

    (a) America

    (b) Britain

2. Merlin is

    (a) a magician and the king's advisor.

    (b) a knight.

3. Merlin took the son of the king and queen because

    (a) he wanted a son of his own.

    (b) he wanted to protect the future king.

4. What appeared in the sky when the baby was born?

    (a) a shining crown

    (b) the head of a huge dragon

5. What does "destiny" mean?

    (a) Things happen that were meant to happen.

    (b) Things cannot be known ahead of time.

6. What happened to King Uther Pendragon a few months after Merlin took his son?

    (a) He was killed in battle.

    (b) He was poisoned.

Now that the reign of Uther Pendragon was over, fierce fighting broke out. Neighboring knights seized each other's land and fought each other. Britain was once again divided.

The turmoil lasted for sixteen years. Then Merlin decided it was time to do something about it.

Now, you must remember that Merlin was a magician, so he did not act in a normal way. Thus, one day the people of London had a great surprise. In the city center, they saw before them a block of white marble with an anvil, which is a heavy block of metal, on top. A sword had been driven into the anvil. Its blade was shimmering, white steel, and the hilt glittered with jewels. On the stone were these words:

Whoso Pulleth Out This Sword

from This Stone and Anvil Is Rightfully

the King of England

The knights and barons pushed and shoved each other so they could try pulling out the sword. The mayor cried out, "Stop, stop. I hereby proclaim that on New Year's Eve all those who feel worthy to try to pull the sword from the stone will be given a chance. And, on that day, there will be a tournament, or contest, between the knights."

Guards were brought in to protect the sword, and the crowds went home.

→ Circle the correct answer.

1. What happened after the end of Uther Pendragon's reign?

(a) The knights got together to choose a new leader.

(b) The knights fought each other.

2. The disorder lasted

(a) six years.

(b) sixteen years.

3. Why do you think Merlin waited so long before letting anyone know that Uther Pendragon had a son?

(a) He wanted Arthur to grow up so he could rule.

(b) He hoped the knights would live peacefully together.

4. What surprise greeted the people one day in London?

(a) a black piece of marble with an anvil and sword

(b) a white piece of marble with an anvil and sword

5. What message did the stone carry?

(a) that the person who pulled the sword from the stone was meant to be king

(b) that the person who pulled the sword from the stone was the strongest man in Britain

6. What was to happen on New Year's Eve?

(a) There was to be a tournament to see who was the strongest.

(b) There was to be a tournament and the chance to pull the sword out of the stone.

The Boy Who Was Meant to Be King: Part 2

Far away from London, in the country, there lived a kind and gracious knight called Sir Ector. He had two sons. Sir Kay, the older of the two, had just been knighted. He was a little full of himself and tended to boss around his younger brother, Arthur. Arthur was a gentle boy. He was sixteen and had been adopted by Sir Ector and his wife when he was a baby. He liked to spend his time in the fields and woods with his animal friends.

A neighboring knight told them about the tournament. Sir Kay was eager to go so he could display his knightly skills. Arthur also wanted to go to help his brother get ready for the contests.

So it was that on New Year's Day, Sir Kay, Arthur, and their father found themselves in London at the tournament.

Sir Kay, with Arthur's help, got ready for his first event. As Arthur was fixing Sir Kay's armor, Sir Kay cried out, "My sword. I don't have my sword!" In his excitement he had left it at the inn where they were staying.

"Quick, Arthur, go and get it," shrieked Sir Kay in a panic.

Arthur quickly obeyed. He jumped on his horse, grabbed the reins, and galloped through the deserted streets to the inn. As Arthur passed the city center, he noticed the shining sword sticking out of the stone. "Oh, great, here's a sword," he said to himself.

The guards had gone, so he reached out and quickly and easily pulled the sword out of the stone.

➔ Checking up: See if you are following the story. Circle the correct answer:

1. Sir Ector and his two sons lived

    (a) in a neighboring town.

    (b) in the country.

2. Arthur spent his time

    (a) learning to be a knight.

    (b) in the fields and woods.

3. The tournament was held on

    (a) the last day of the year.

    (b) the first day of the year.

4. Sir Kay forgot

    (a) his sword.

    (b) his armor.

5. When Arthur rushed to find a sword for his brother,

    (a) he ran through the streets.

    (b) he rode through the streets.

6. Arthur tried to take the sword because

    (a) he wanted to help his brother in the tournament.

    (b) he wanted to be king.

When Sir Kay saw the sword he turned deathly white.

"Where did you get it?" he asked, already knowing the answer. Then he said, "Get father."

Sir Ector came quickly. He recognized the sword immediately.

"Father, I have the sword. Doesn't that mean I am the rightful king?" asked Sir Kay.

"How can this be? How did you get it?" asked Sir Ector.

"I—I—pulled it from the stone," lied Sir Kay.

"Then you should put it back," his father said.

Sir Ector, Sir Kay, and Arthur went to the stone.

"Now put it back," Sir Ector told Sir Kay, fearing his son was not telling the truth.

Sir Kay tried, but the sharp point would not go into the stone.

"Now tell me, how did you get the sword?" Sir Ector asked quietly.

"Arthur brought it to me," Sir Kay confessed.

"Is that true, Arthur?" Sir Ector asked, as a wave of fear swept over him.

"Yes, Father, please forgive me, but I was going to put it back as soon as Kay had finished with it."

"Put it back now, son," Sir Ector said. And Arthur did.

Now Sir Ector knew who this boy really was whom he and his wife had raised as their son and loved dearly.

Slowly Sir Ector knelt down.

"Father, what are you doing?" asked Arthur.

Sir Ector pointed to the words on the stone and Arthur turned pale.

"But I am your son. How could I be king?" Arthur asked.

"When your mother and I adopted you, we did not know who you were. But now I realize that you must be the son of Uther Pendragon, who died sixteen years ago."

"But I don't want to be king. I don't want to leave you," cried Arthur.

"Arthur, it is your destiny. But I will stay with you."

Just then, Merlin appeared in a swirl of mist. He told Arthur to come to the sword-pulling contest.

Arthur was to wait until everyone had tried, and then he would have his turn. This would prove to everyone that he was the rightful heir to the throne.

 And that is what happened. Everyone was amazed when the slim, young boy of sixteen gently and slowly pulled the sword out of the stone. There was complete silence. Then, as Arthur, with new confidence, raised the sword above his head, there were loud cheers.

Arthur was crowned and became a great and good king.

➜ Circle the correct answer.

1. When Sir Kay saw the sword, what did he say to Arthur?

    (a) "Great, I must be king."

    (b) "Get father."

2. Did Sir Ector believe Sir Kay when he said he had pulled the sword from the stone?

    (a) yes

    (b) no

3. Why could Sir Kay not put the sword back into the stone?

(a) He was not meant to be king.

(b) He was not strong enough.

4. Why did a wave of fear sweep over Sir Ector when he realized Arthur had pulled out the sword?

(a) because Arthur was a thief

(b) because he knew that Arthur was the heir to the throne

5. Why did Sir Ector make Arthur put back the sword?

(a) He wanted to make sure that Arthur had power over the sword.

(b) He was afraid Arthur would be accused of stealing.

6. Was Arthur happy when he realized he was the king?

(a) yes

(b) no

7. What did Merlin tell Arthur to do?

(a) tell everyone that he was the king

(b) wait for his turn after all the other contestants failed to pull out the sword

8. Did the people accept Arthur as their king.

(a) yes

(b) no

Write your own story set in a time long ago. Before you write, make notes about your characters, the setting where the story takes place, and the events—what happens in the story. Use colorful words for your descriptions and dialogue to make your characters seem like real people.

_____

_____

_____

_____

_____

_____

_____

_____

_____

_____

_____

_____

_____

_____

_____

_____